Popular Complete Smart Series

Complete
Canadian
Curriculum

LUKE

Grade
1

Mathematics

English

Social Studies

Science

MATHEMATICS

* The Canadian penny is no longer in circulation. It is used in the units to show money amounts to the cent.

Comparison

- Compare the sizes, heights, and lengths of different things.
- Use words such as "bigger", "biggest", "taller", and "tallest" to describe objects.

I'm the biggest.

I'm smaller than the dog.

Colour the bigger one.

① ② ③

Draw the pictures.

④ a smaller house

⑤ a bigger butterfly

⑥ a smaller cat

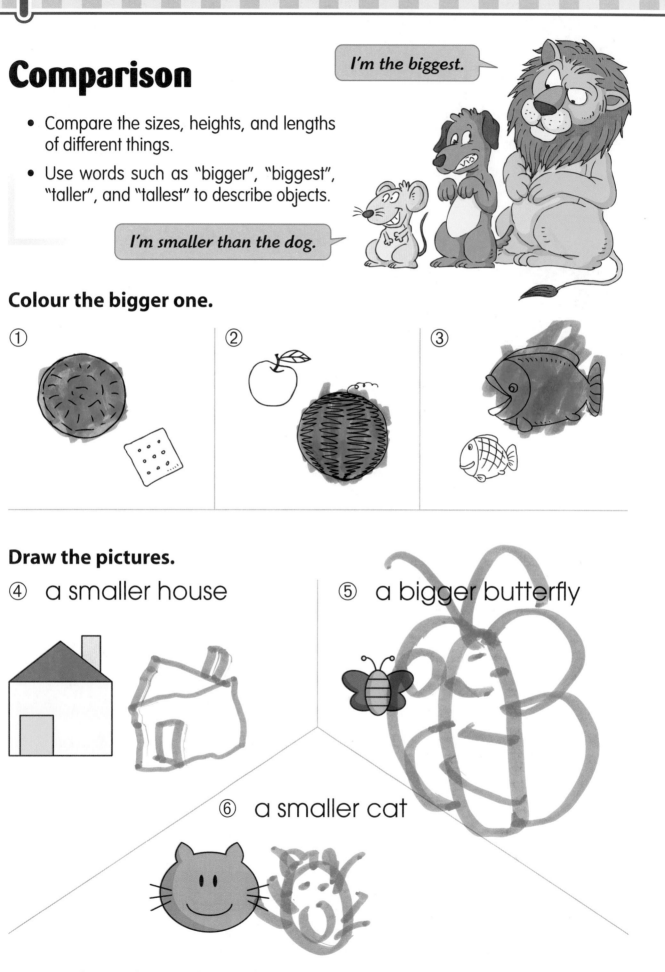

Check ✔ the taller one.

Colour the longer one.

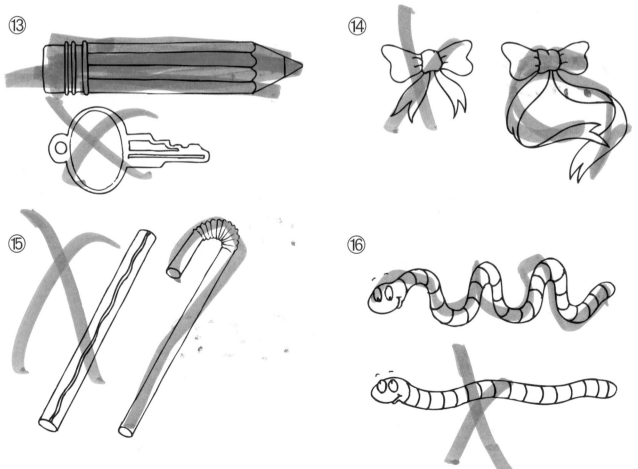

Put each group of things in order. Write the letters.

⑰

From longest to shortest:

B. C A

⑱

From smallest to biggest:

B A C

⑲

From biggest to smallest:

CAB

⑳
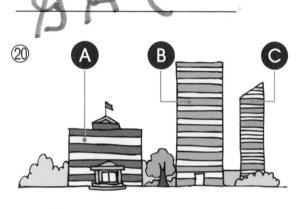

From tallest to shortest:

B C A

㉑

From biggest to smallest:

A C B

From tallest to shortest:

A C B

Draw one bracelet that is the same length as the one shown. Then draw one that is longer.

㉒

Look at the picture. Fill in the blanks with the correct words.

longer	longest
taller	tallest
shorter	shortest
same	
smaller	smallest
bigger	biggest

Mrs. Green Amy Tom Sue

㉓ Amy and Sue are the _____SAME_____ height.

㉔ Tom's slippers are _____BIGGER_____ than Amy's slippers.

㉕ Tom's slippers are _____BIGGEST_____.

㉖ Amy's hair is _____LONGEST_____ than Mrs. Green's hair.

㉗ Tom's hair is _____LONGER_____ than Sue's hair.

㉘ The train is _____SHORTER_____ than the skipping rope.

More about Comparison

- Compare the widths, thicknesses, and weights of different objects.
- Compare numbers of different groups of objects.

> *This is the widest that I can open my mouth.*

Colour the wider one in each pair.

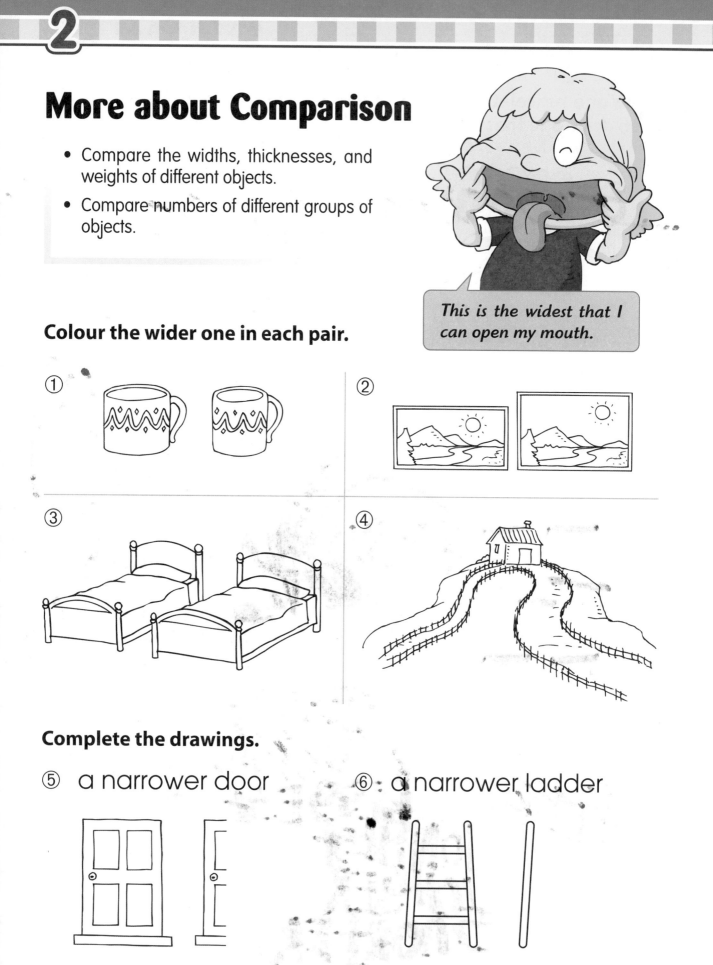

①

②

③

④

Complete the drawings.

⑤ a narrower door

⑥ a narrower ladder

Colour the thicker one.

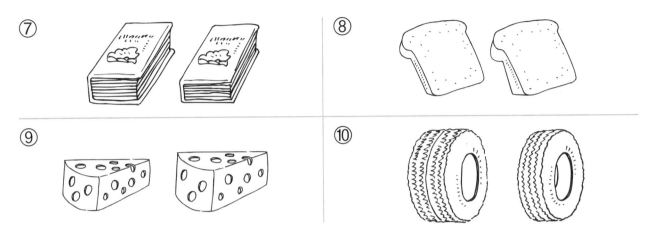

⑦   ⑧

⑨   ⑩

Complete the drawings.

⑪ **a thicker sandwich**

⑫ **a thinner hamburger**

Look at the pictures. Fill in the blanks with letters.

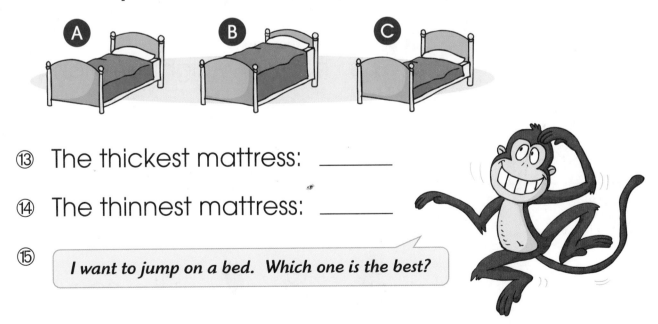

A   B   C

⑬ The thickest mattress: _____

⑭ The thinnest mattress: _____

⑮ I want to jump on a bed. Which one is the best?

_____

Circle ◯ the heavier one in each pair.

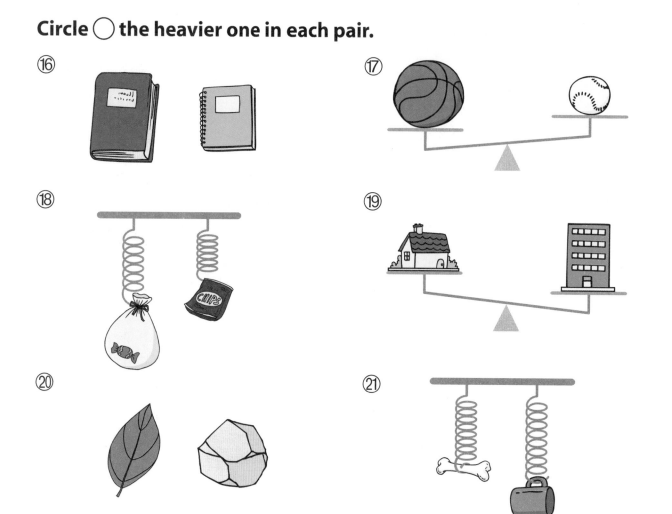

Look at the picture. Circle ◯ the correct words or picture.

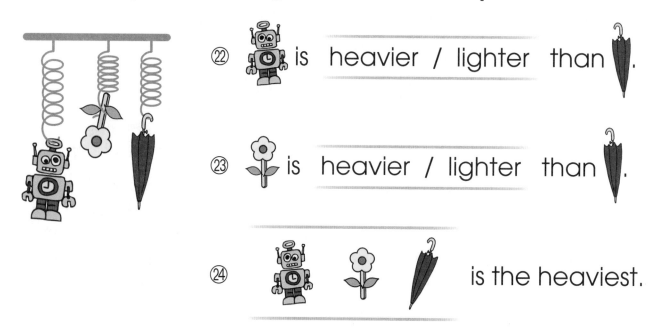

22 🤖 is heavier / lighter than ☂.

23 🌸 is heavier / lighter than ☂.

24 🤖 🌸 ☂ is the heaviest.

Circle ◯ the group with more items.

㉕

㉖

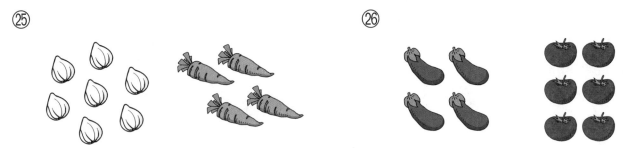

Colour the group with the most items.

㉗

㉘

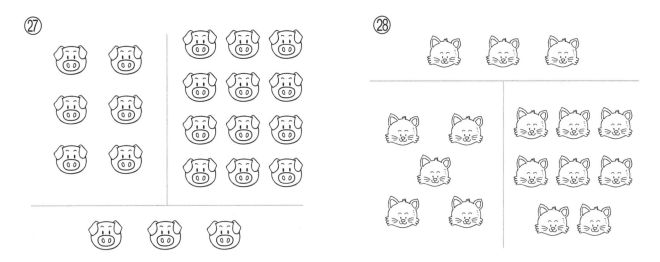

Look at the pictures. Answer the questions.

㉙ Which pond has the most fish? _____

㉚ Which pond has the fewest fish? _____

㉛ Which pond has more fish than **C** ? _____

Ordering and Sorting

My toys.

- Order things by their sizes, heights, numbers, etc.
- Sort things out with simple rules.
- Make rules to organize things.

Ben's toys

Check ✔ the group with objects put in order.

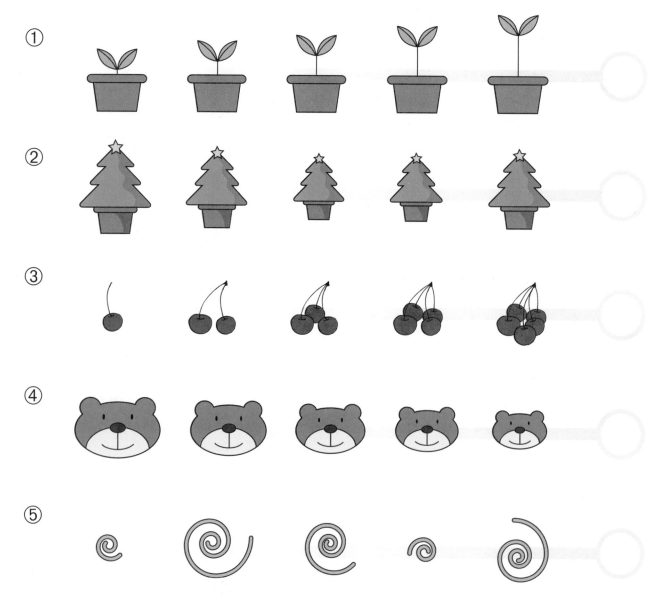

①

②

③

④

⑤

Put the things in the correct order. Write the letters.

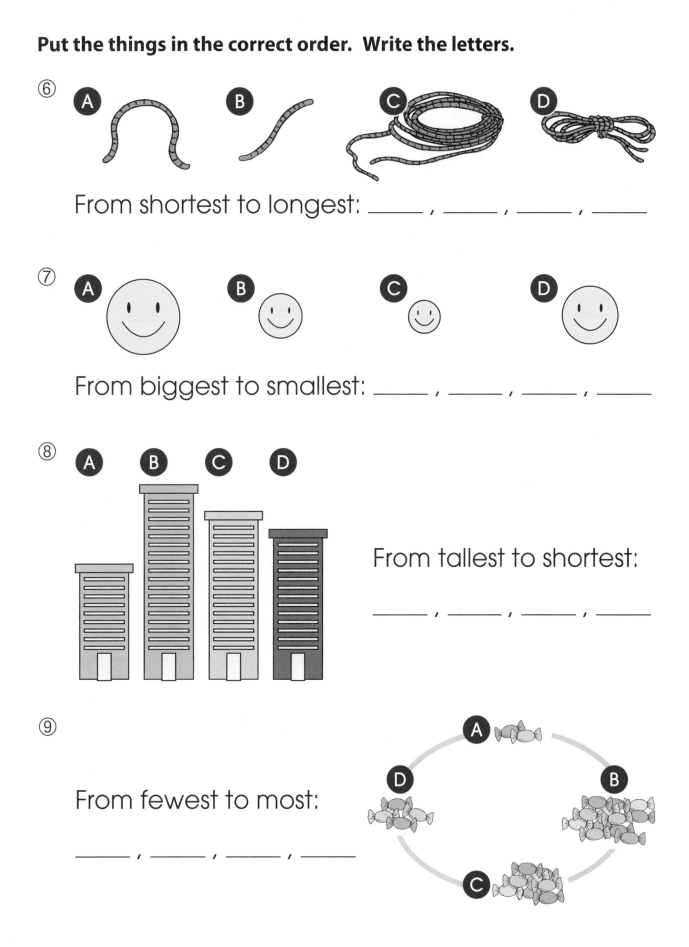

⑥ A B C D

From shortest to longest: _____ , _____ , _____ , _____

⑦ A B C D

From biggest to smallest: _____ , _____ , _____ , _____

⑧ A B C D

From tallest to shortest:

_____ , _____ , _____ , _____

⑨

From fewest to most:

_____ , _____ , _____ , _____

A B C D

Cross out ✘ the item that does not belong in each group.

⑩

⑪

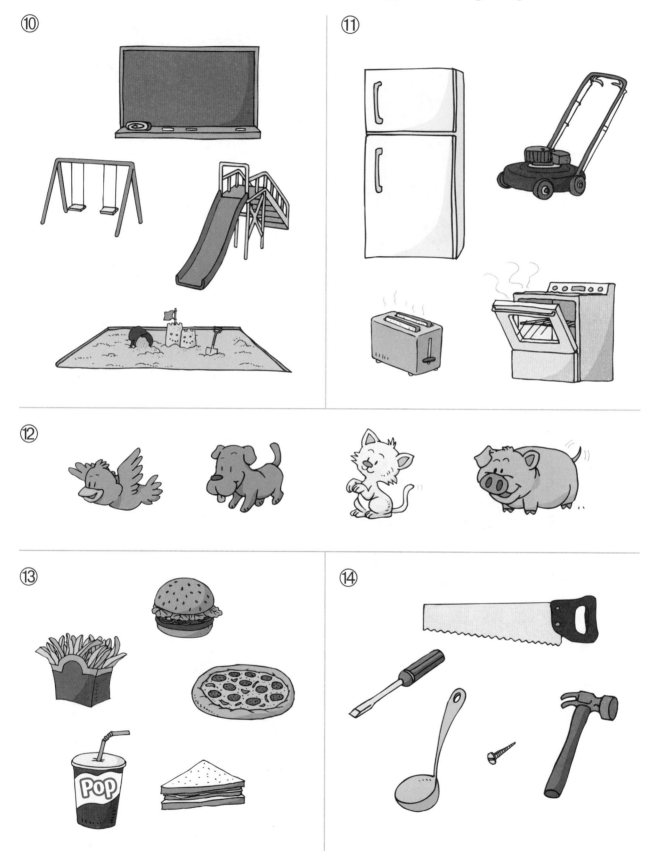

⑫

⑬

⑭

When you write the rule to sort some items, look carefully to find the common characteristic of the items first. There may be more than one way to sort them.

e.g.

Tools: __A, C__

Utensils: __B, D__

Look at the items in each group. Write the sorting rule. Then sort the items.

Sequencing

- Understand the sequence of some events in daily life.
- Use ordinal numbers to describe the position of people or objects in a group.

Look at the pictures.   Put them in the correct sequence.   Write the letters.

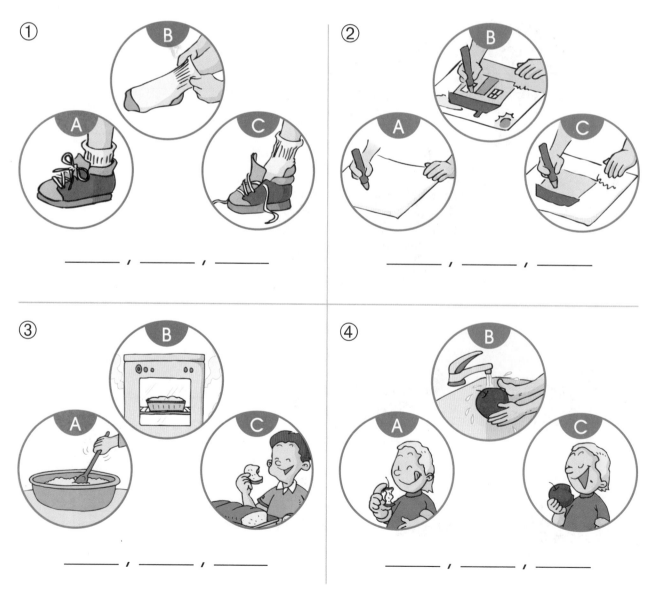

① _____ , _____ , _____

② _____ , _____ , _____

③ _____ , _____ , _____

④ _____ , _____ , _____

M A T H E M A T I C S

Put the pictures in the correct sequence. Write the letters. Then colour the picture that comes next.

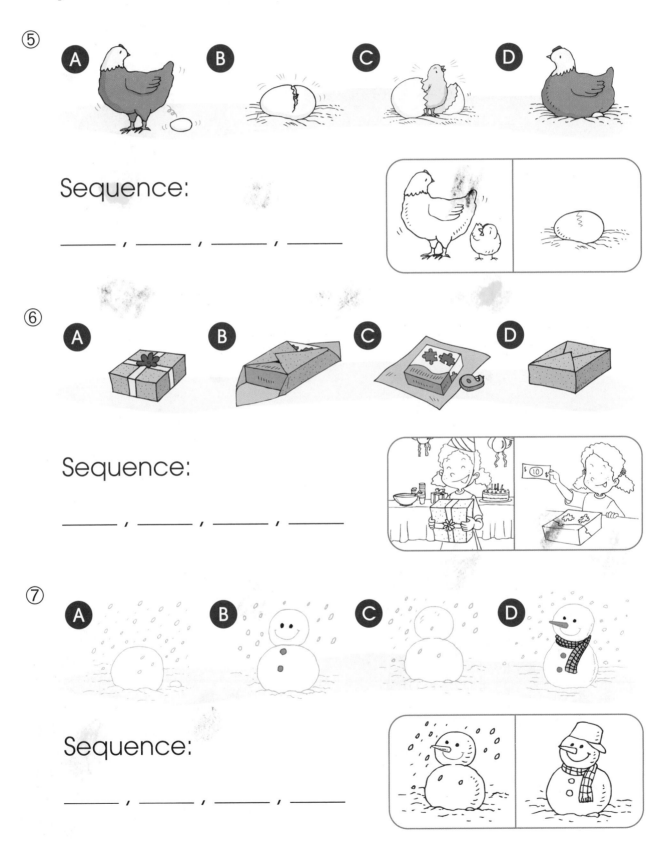

⑤ A   B   C   D

Sequence:

_____ , _____ , _____ , _____

⑥ A   B   C   D

Sequence:

_____ , _____ , _____ , _____

⑦ A   B   C   D

Sequence:

_____ , _____ , _____ , _____

Look at each group of things. Colour the first one yellow, the third one blue, and the sixth one red. Then find the position.

⑧ This apple is the _____ .

⑨ The position of 🐟 : _____

⑩ The position of 🎈 : _____

⑪ The position of ⚽ : _____

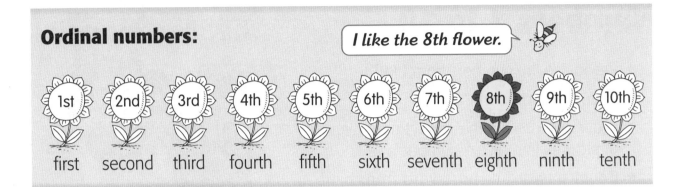

Ordinal numbers:

I like the 8th flower.

1st	2nd	3rd	4th	5th	6th	7th	8th	9th	10th
first	second	third	fourth	fifth	sixth	seventh	eighth	ninth	tenth

Write the ordinal numbers in words.

⑫ 5th _____

⑬ 7th _____

⑭ 2nd _____

⑮ 8th _____

⑯ 1st _____

⑰ 4th _____

Look at the pictures.   Write the correct ordinal numbers.

⑱

I'm the _____ and you're the _____ .

⑲

You have a chain of food. The _____ , _____ , and _____ are sausages.

Numbers 1 to 10

- Recognize the numbers from 1 to 10.
- Write the numbers in words.
- Draw or cross out the correct number of pictures to match a number.
- Count forward or backward from a given number.

5 gifts.

Count and write the numbers.

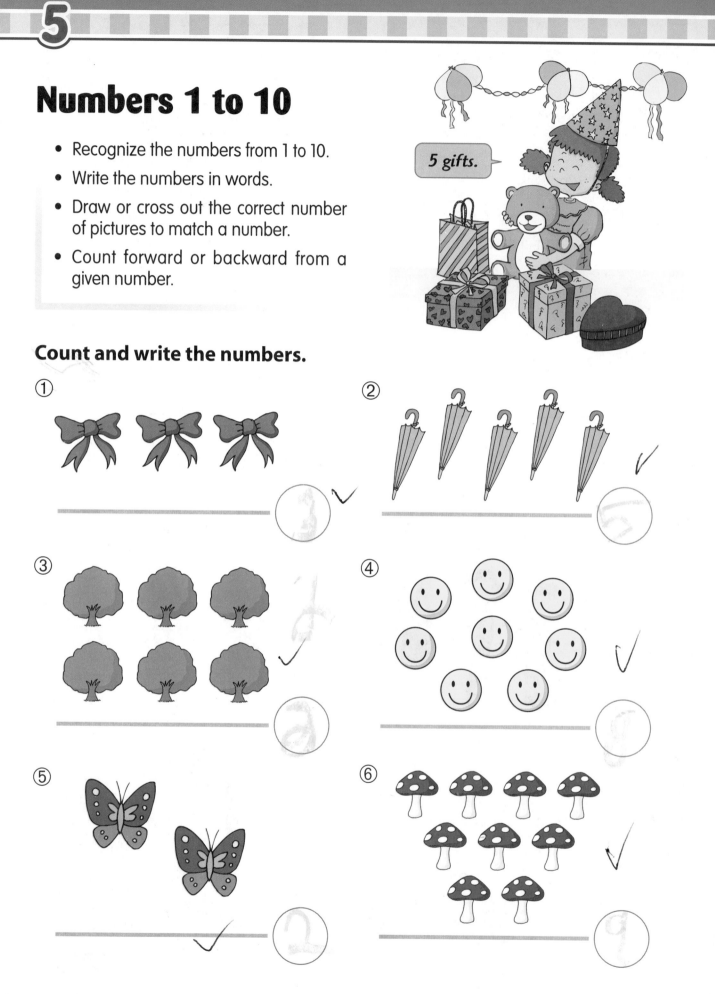

① _____

② _____

③ _____

④ _____

⑤ _____

⑥ _____

Count and write the numbers in words.

⑦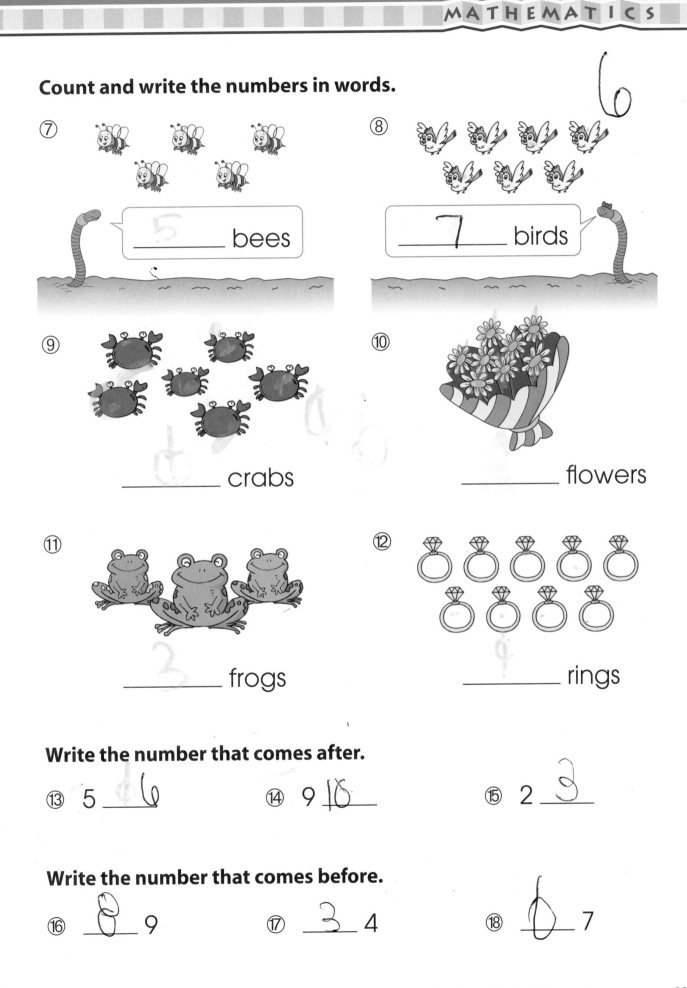

_____5_____ bees

⑧

_____7_____ birds

⑨

_____ crabs

⑩

_____ flowers

⑪

_____ frogs

⑫

_____ rings

Write the number that comes after.

⑬ 5 __6__

⑭ 9 __10__

⑮ 2 __3__

Write the number that comes before.

⑯ __8__ 9

⑰ __3__ 4

⑱ __6__ 7

Complete Canadian Curriculum • **Grade 1**   23

Draw 1 more item in each group. Then count and write the number.

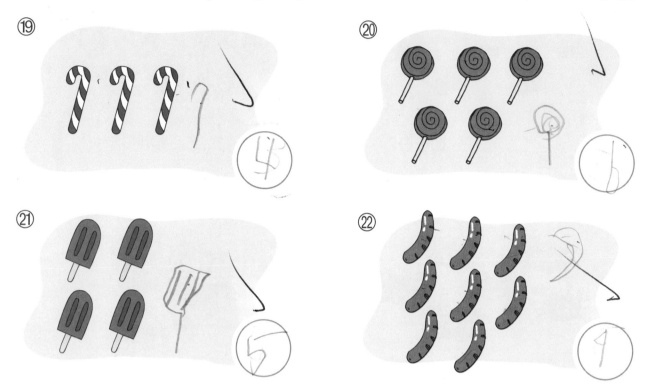

⑲

⑳

㉑

㉒

Draw or cross out ✗ the correct number of pictures to match the given numbers.

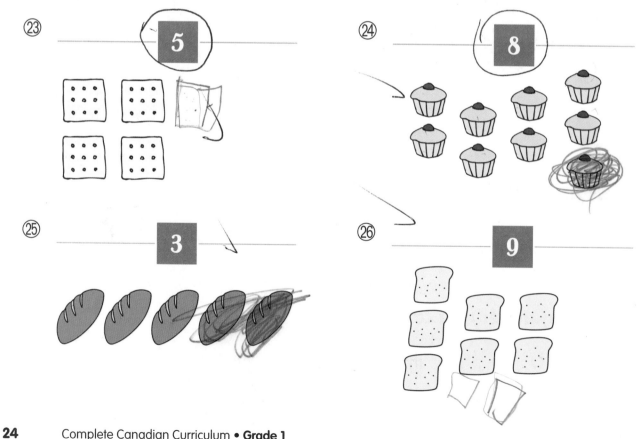

㉓   5

㉔   8

㉕   3

㉖   9

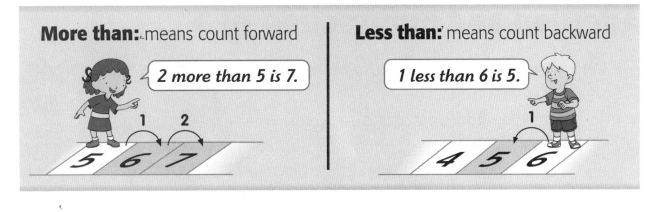

More than: means count forward

2 more than 5 is 7.

Less than: means count backward

1 less than 6 is 5.

Fill in the missing numbers.

㉗ 1, 2, __3__, __4__, 5

㉘ 4, 5, __6__, __7__, 8

㉙ 7, 6, __5__, __4__, 3

㉚ 10, 9, __8__, __7__, 6

㉛ 5, __6__, __7__, __8__, 9

㉜ 8, __7__, __6__, 5, __4__

Colour the correct number of boxes. Then fill in the blanks.

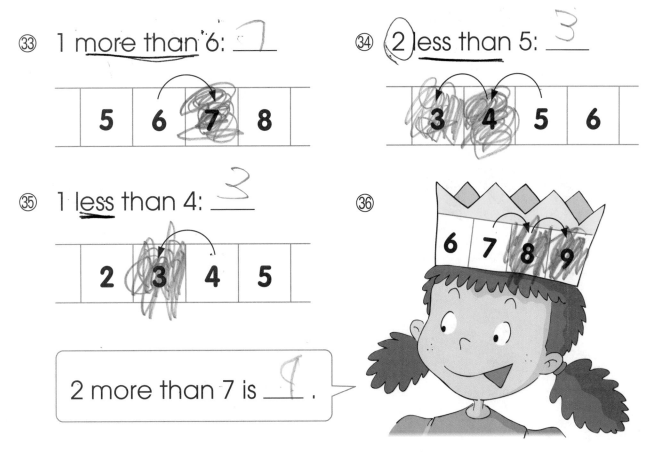

㉝ 1 more than 6: __7__

| 5 | 6 | 7 | 8 |

㉞ 2 less than 5: __3__

| 3 | 4 | 5 | 6 |

㉟ 1 less than 4: __3__

| 2 | 3 | 4 | 5 |

㊱

| 6 | 7 | 8 | 9 |

2 more than 7 is __9__ .

Addition and Subtraction of 1

- Put 1 more item in a group and use words to describe addition.
- Take away 1 item from a group and use words to describe subtraction.

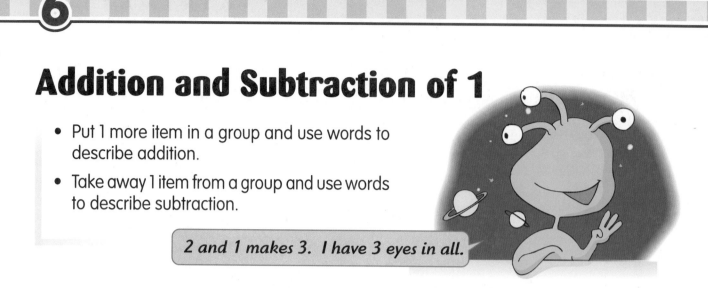

> 2 and 1 makes 3. I have 3 eyes in all.

Count and write the number of items in each group. Then draw 1 more item and tell how many items there are in all.

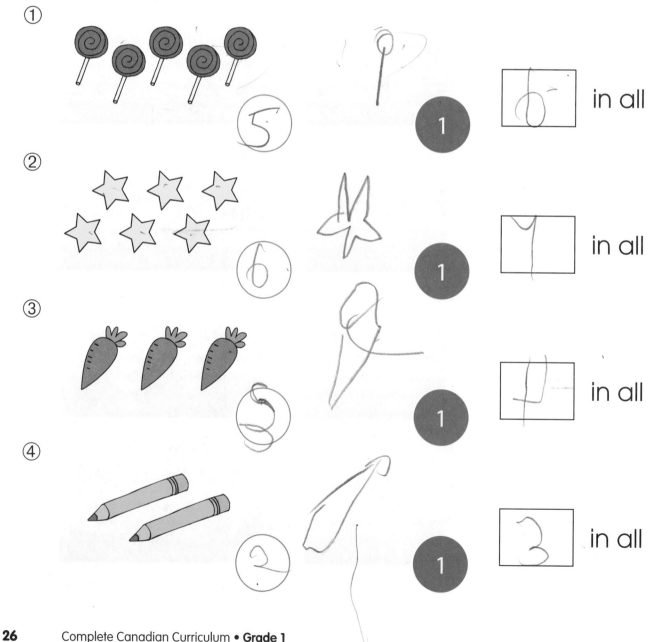

① 5   1   6 in all

② 6   1   in all

③ 3   1   in all

④ 2   1   3 in all

Draw the correct number of items to show the total. Then write the numbers to match the group of items.

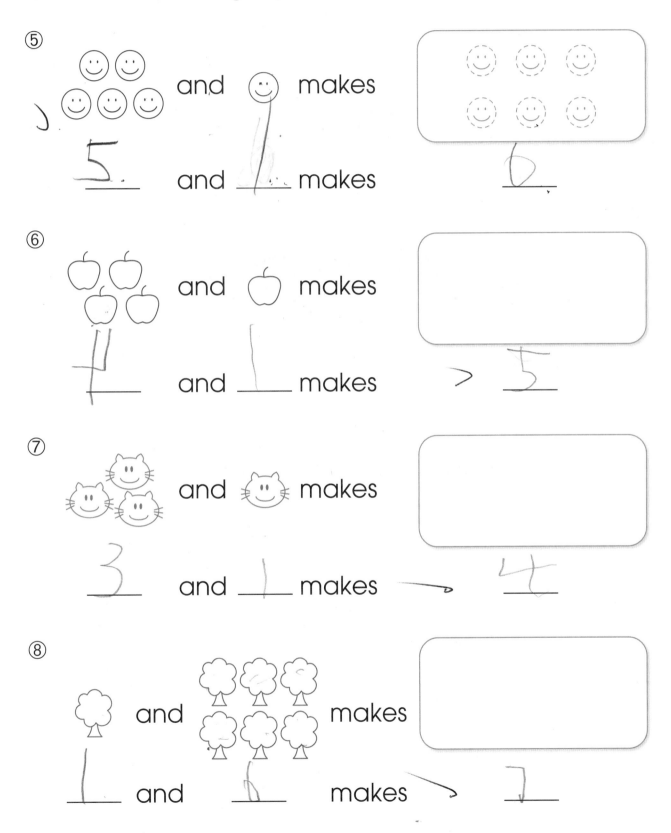

⑤ and makes

5 and 1 makes 6

⑥ and makes

4 and ___ makes > 5

⑦ and makes

3 and 1 makes → 4

⑧ and makes

1 and 6 makes → 7

Count and write how many items there are in each group. Then put a cross ✗ on one item and tell how many items are left.

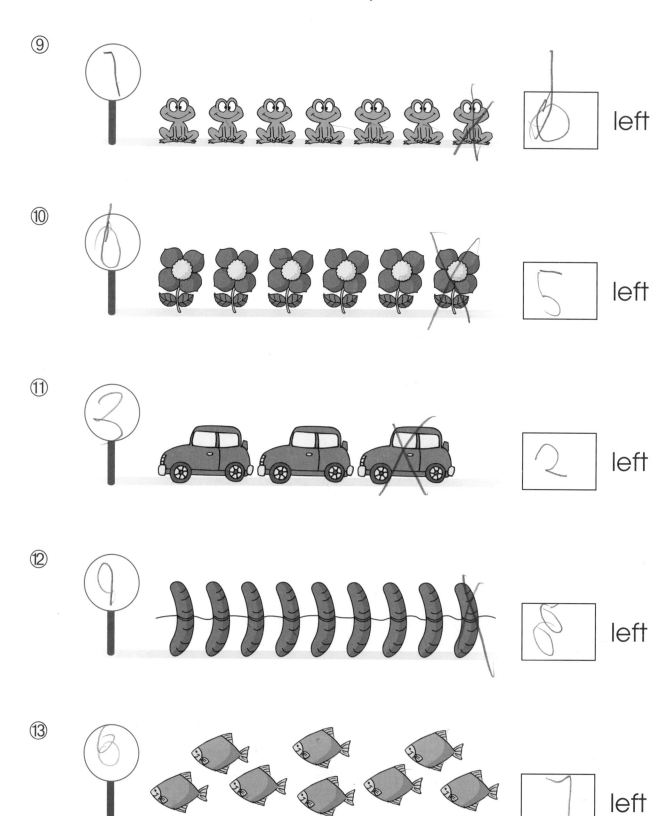

⑨ 7 — 6 left

⑩ 0 — 5 left

⑪ 3 — 2 left

⑫ 9 — 8 left

⑬ 6 — 7 left

Cross out ✗ one item in each group.   Then fill in the blanks with numbers.

⑭ 6 take away 1 leaves 5

⑮ 6 take away 1 leaves 5

⑯ 16 take away 1 leaves 9

⑰ 7 take away 1 leaves 6

⑱ 5 take away 1 leaves 4 .

Addition and Subtraction Facts to 6

$$3 + 2 = 5$$
$$3 - 2 = 1$$

- Add and subtract 1-digit numbers with the help of pictures.
- Do addition and subtraction up to 6.
- Understand the use of "+", "–", and "=" to describe addition and subtraction problems.

I have 5 fish in all, and I have 1 more big fish than small fish.

Draw the correct number of things. Then complete the addition sentences.

① 2 more

3 and ___ makes ___

② 2 more

2 and ___ makes ___

③ 1 more

4 and ___ makes ___

④ 3 more

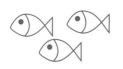

3 and ___ makes ___

Fill in the blanks with numbers to match the pictures.

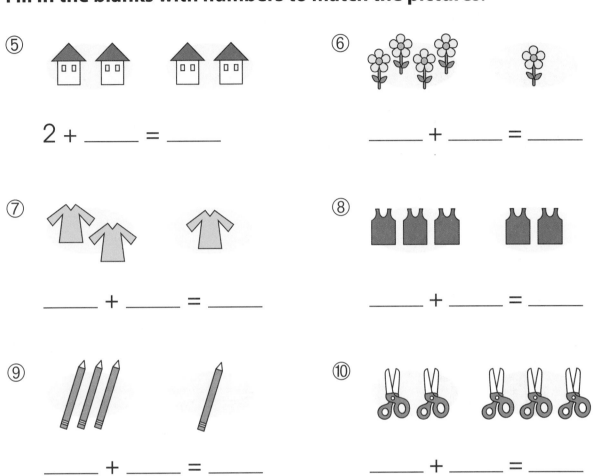

⑤ $2 + \underline{\quad} = \underline{\quad}$

⑥ $\underline{\quad} + \underline{\quad} = \underline{\quad}$

⑦ $\underline{\quad} + \underline{\quad} = \underline{\quad}$

⑧ $\underline{\quad} + \underline{\quad} = \underline{\quad}$

⑨ $\underline{\quad} + \underline{\quad} = \underline{\quad}$

⑩ $\underline{\quad} + \underline{\quad} = \underline{\quad}$

Draw your own pictures to match the addition sentences. Then find the answers.

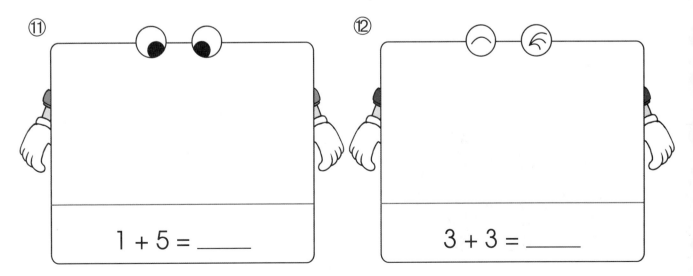

⑪ $1 + 5 = \underline{\quad}$

⑫ $3 + 3 = \underline{\quad}$

Cross out ✗ the correct number of pictures. Then complete the subtraction sentences.

⑬ Cross out 1 fish.

3 take away _____ leaves _____

3 - _____ = _____

⑭ Cross out 2 pears.

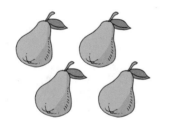

4 take away _____ leaves _____

4 - _____ = _____

⑮ Cross out 3 cats.

7 take away _____ leaves _____

7 - _____ = _____

⑯ Cross out 1 tree.

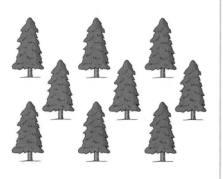

9 take away _____ leaves _____

9 - _____ = _____

Steps to do word problems:

 **1st** Read the problem once.
2nd Underline the key words, such as "in all" and "left".
3rd Write a number sentence.
4th Find the answer.

Complete the number sentences to match the pictures.

⑰ _____ + _____ = _____

⑱ _____ − _____ = _____

⑲ _____ − _____ = _____

⑳ _____ + _____ = _____

Help the cat solve the problems.

㉑ There are 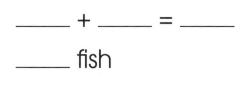 and .... How many fish are there in all?

_____ + _____ = _____

_____ fish

㉒

How many fish are left?

_____ − _____ = _____

_____ fish

Addition and Subtraction Facts to 10

- Add and subtract 1-digit numbers with or without the help of pictures.
- Do addition and subtraction up to 10.
- Do vertical addition and subtraction.

She has 7 rings in all.

$$\begin{array}{r} 3 \\ + 4 \\ \hline 7 \end{array}$$

Fill in the blanks with numbers to match the pictures.

① $4 + 5 = 9$

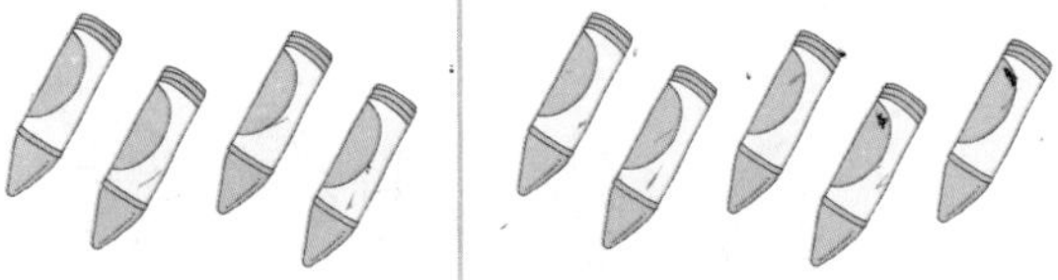

② $5 + 2 = 7$

③ $6 + 3 = 9$

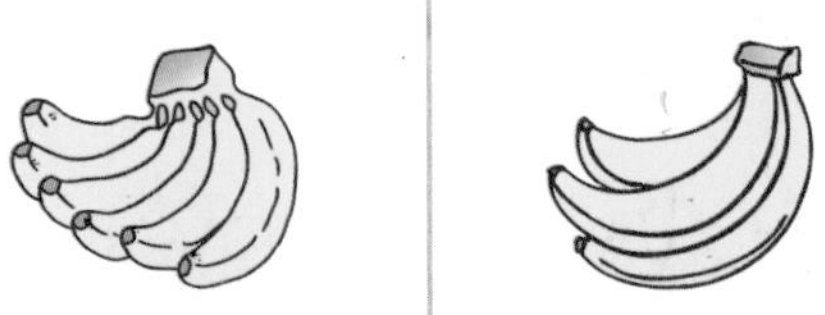

④ $2 + 6 = 8$

⑤ $5 + 2 = 7$

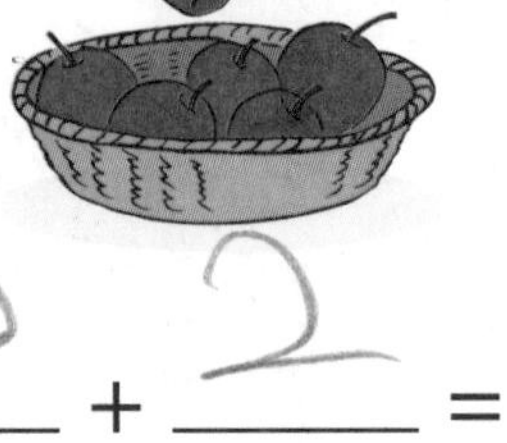

⑥ $4 + 4 = 8$

Find the answers with the help of the picture.

⑦ 3 + 5 = 8

⑧ 4 + 2 = 6

⑨ 6 + 1 = 7

⑩ 5 + 5 = 10

⑪ 3 + 4 = 7

⑫ 8 + 1 = 9

⑬ 7 + 2 = 9

⑭ 2 + 3 = 5

Draw 10 apples in the tree. Then find the answers with the help of the apples.

⑮ 4 + 5 = 9

⑯ 3 + 1 = 4

⑰ 2 + 6 = 8

⑱ 4 + 4 = 8

⑲ 5 + 2 = 7

⑳ 1 + 9 = 10

㉑ 3 + 3 = 6

㉒ 2 + 4 = 6

㉓ 5 + 3 = 8

㉔ 1 + 6 = 7

Fill in the blanks with numbers to match the pictures.

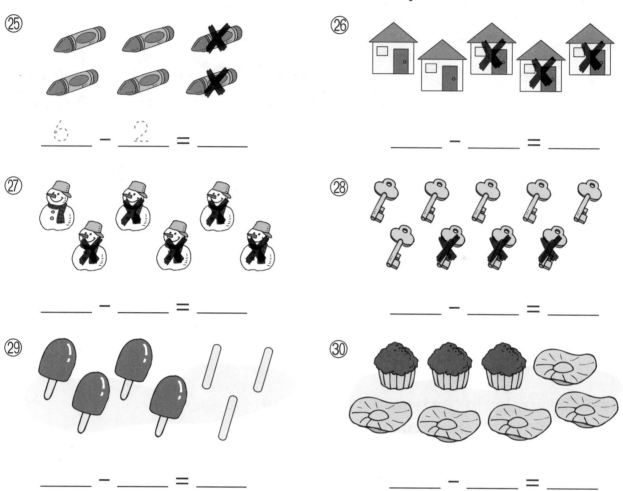

㉕ _6_ – _2_ = _____

㉖ _____ – _____ = _____

㉗ _____ – _____ = _____

㉘ _____ – _____ = _____

㉙ _____ – _____ = _____

㉚ _____ – _____ = _____

Find the answers with the help of the picture.

㉛ 9 – 4 = _____

㉜ 8 – 5 = _____

㉝ 6 – 1 = _____

㉞ 9 – 7 = _____

㉟ 10 – 3 = _____

㊱ 8 – 4 = _____

㊲ 8 – 2 = _____

㊳ 7 – 3 = _____

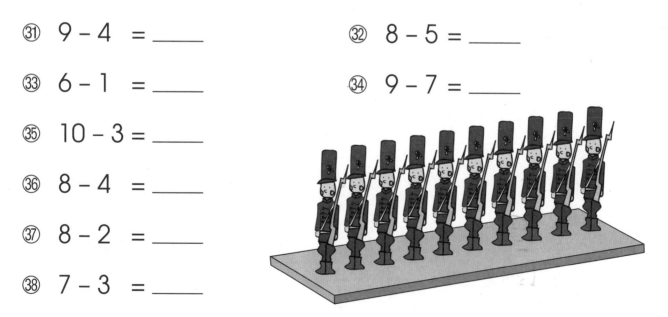

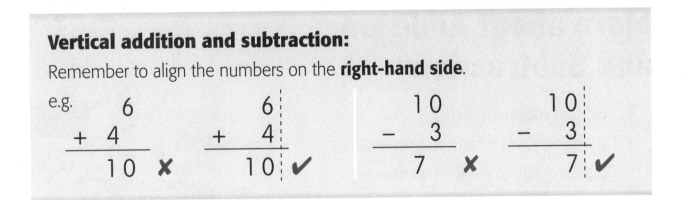

Vertical addition and subtraction:

Remember to align the numbers on the **right-hand side**.

e.g.

```
    6          6           10          10
  + 4        + 4         -  3        -  3
  ----       ----        ----        ----
   10  ✗      10  ✔         7  ✗          7  ✔
```

Find the answers.

(39)
```
      5
  (+) 3
  -------
    8
```

(40)
```
      7
  (−) 4
  -------
    3
```

(41)
```
      9
  (−) 6
  -------
    3
```

(42)
```
      4
  (+) 4
  -------
    8
```

(43)
```
      6
  (−) 2
  -------
    4
```

(44)
```
      7
  (+) 3
  -------
   10
```

(45)
```
      5
  (−) 1
  -------
    4
```

(46)
```
      8
  (+) 1
  -------
    9
```

(47)
```
     10
  (−) 6
  -------
    4
```

(48)

> I had 10 rings at first, but now I only have these rings left. How many rings did I lose?

```
   (10)
  (−) 6
  -------
    4
```

_4_ rings

9

More about Addition and Subtraction

I have 0 cups of juice left.

$4 - 4 = 0$

- Add and subtract with 0.
- Do addition and subtraction up to 10.
- Do subtraction to get 0 as an answer.
- Use addition and subtraction to solve word problems.

Find the answers with the help of the picture.

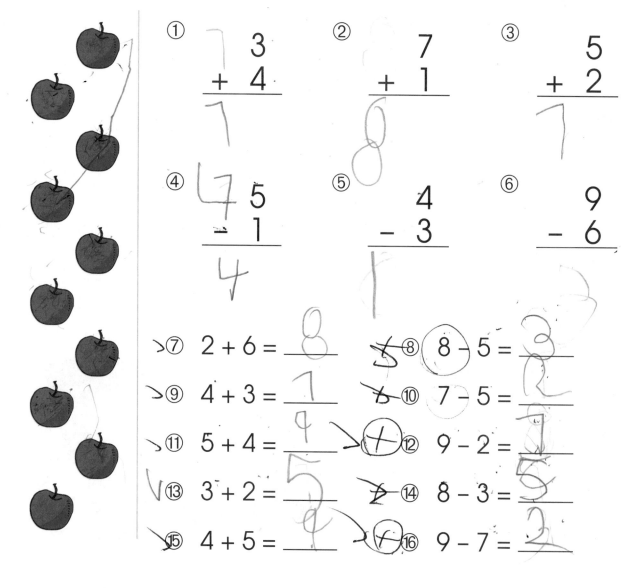

①
$$\begin{array}{r} 3 \\ + 4 \\ \hline 7 \end{array}$$

②
$$\begin{array}{r} 7 \\ + 1 \\ \hline 8 \end{array}$$

③
$$\begin{array}{r} 5 \\ + 2 \\ \hline 7 \end{array}$$

④
$$\begin{array}{r} 5 \\ - 1 \\ \hline 4 \end{array}$$

⑤
$$\begin{array}{r} 4 \\ - 3 \\ \hline 1 \end{array}$$

⑥
$$\begin{array}{r} 9 \\ - 6 \\ \hline \end{array}$$

⑦ $2 + 6 =$ ___ 8

⑧ $8 - 5 =$ ___ 3

⑨ $4 + 3 =$ ___ 7

⑩ $7 - 5 =$ ___

⑪ $5 + 4 =$ ___ 9

⑫ $9 - 2 =$ ___ 7

⑬ $3 + 2 =$ ___ 5

⑭ $8 - 3 =$ ___ 5

⑮ $4 + 5 =$ ___

⑯ $9 - 7 =$ ___ 2

Look at the pictures. Complete the number sentences.

⑰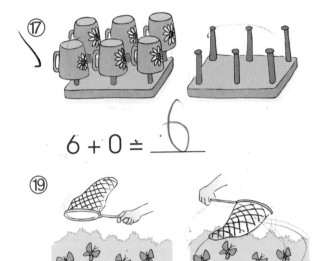

$6 + 0 = \underline{6}$

⑱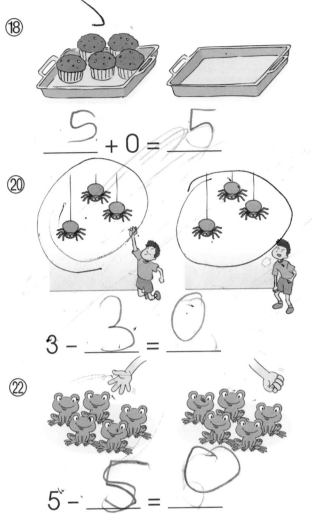

$\underline{5} + 0 = \underline{5}$

⑲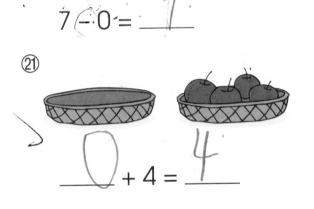

$7 - 0 = \underline{7}$

⑳

$3 - \underline{3} = \underline{0}$

㉑

$\underline{0} + 4 = \underline{4}$

㉒

$5 - \underline{5} = \underline{0}$

Find the answers.

㉓
$$\begin{array}{r} 9 \\ + 0 \\ \hline 9 \end{array}$$

㉔
$$\begin{array}{r} 8 \\ - 0 \\ \hline \end{array}$$

㉕
$$\begin{array}{r} 6 \\ - 0 \\ \hline \end{array}$$

㉖ $1 + 0 = \underline{}$

㉗ $5 - 0 = \underline{5}$

㉘ $4 - 0 = \underline{4}$

㉙ $0 + 7 = \underline{7}$

㉚ $3 - 0 = \underline{3}$

㉛ $2 + 0 = \underline{}$

Look at the pictures. Complete the number sentences.

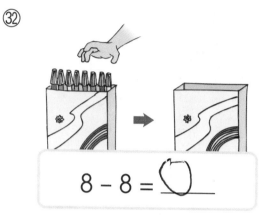

32
$$8 - 8 = \underline{0}$$

33
$$5 - 5 = \underline{0}$$

Find the answers.

34
$$\begin{array}{r} 3 \\ 3 \\ \hline 0 \end{array}$$

35
$$\begin{array}{r} 4 \\ -\ 4 \\ \hline 0 \end{array}$$

36
$$\begin{array}{r} 6 \\ -\ 6 \\ \hline 0 \end{array}$$

37 $8 - 8 = \underline{0}$

38 $7 - 7 = \underline{0}$

39 $9 - 9 = \underline{0}$

40 $1 - 1 = \underline{0}$

41 I have 2 bones. If I eat 2 bones, how many bones will I have left?

$$\begin{array}{r} 2 \\ -\ \\ \hline 0 \end{array}$$

$\underline{0}$ bones

42 David the Dog has 5 bones. If he gives me all his bones, how many bones will he have left?

$$\begin{array}{r} 5 \\ -\ \\ \hline 0 \end{array}$$

$\underline{0}$ bones

"**+**": means "add" or "plus" "**-**": means "take away" or "minus" "**=**": means "equal to"	Addition key words: in all, total Subtraction key words: fewer, more...than, left

Solve the problems.

㊷ Judy has 5 red balls and 2 green balls. How many balls does Judy have in all?

$5 \oplus 2 = 7$ 7 balls

㊸ Mrs. Green has 7 big apples and 3 small apples. How many more big apples than small apples does she have?

$7 \ominus 3 = 4$ 4 more

㊹ There are 4 boys and 4 girls playing in a park. How many children are there in the park?

$4 \oplus 4 = 8$ 8 children

㊺

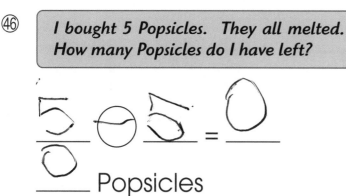

> I bought 5 Popsicles. They all melted. How many Popsicles do I have left?

$5 \ominus 5 = 0$

0 Popsicles

Numbers 1 to 20

- Recognize the numbers from 1 to 20.
- Count forward or backward from a given number.
- Tell whether a number is even or odd.

I have 13 blueberries.

Count and write the numbers.

① 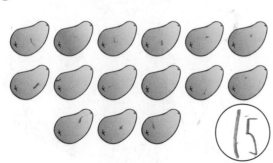 6

② 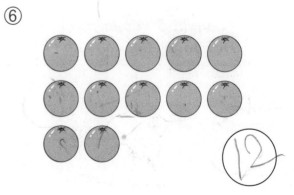 8

③ 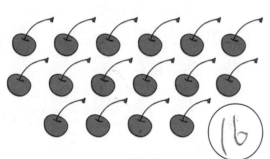 16

④ 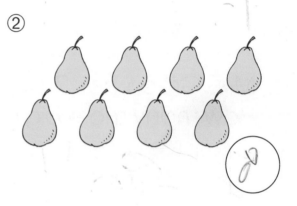 14

⑤ 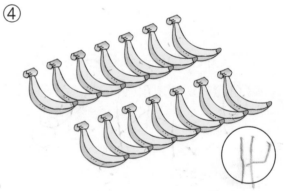 15

⑥ 12

Write the number that comes after.

⑦ 15 _16_

⑧ 12 _13_

⑨ 19 _20_

⑩ 13 _14_

⑪ 10 _11_

⑫ 16 _17_ 77

Write the number that comes before.

⑬ _8_ 9

⑭ _16_ 17

⑮ _11_ 12

⑯ _15_ 16

⑰ _9_ 10

⑱ _4_ 5

Fill in the missing numbers.

⑲ 12 | 13 | _14_ | _15_ | _16_ | 17 | _18_ | 19

⑳ 19 | 18 | _17_ | _16_ | 15 | _14_ | _13_ | 12

㉑ 7 8 _9_ _10_ 11 _12_ _13_ 14

㉒ 9 8 _7_ _6_ 5 _4_ _3_ 2

㉓ 10 11 _12_ _13_ _14_ 15 _16_ 17

㉔ 16 15 _14_ _13_ _12_ 11 _10_ 9

Put the numbers in order from least to greatest.

㉕

5   13   9

5 9 13

㉖

10   2   16

2 10 16

㉗ 4, 10, 8, 5

In order: _4 5 8 10_

㉘ 3, 7, 11, 2

In order: _2 3 7 11_

Draw arrows on the number lines. Then fill in the blanks.

㉙ 2 less than 14 is _12_ .

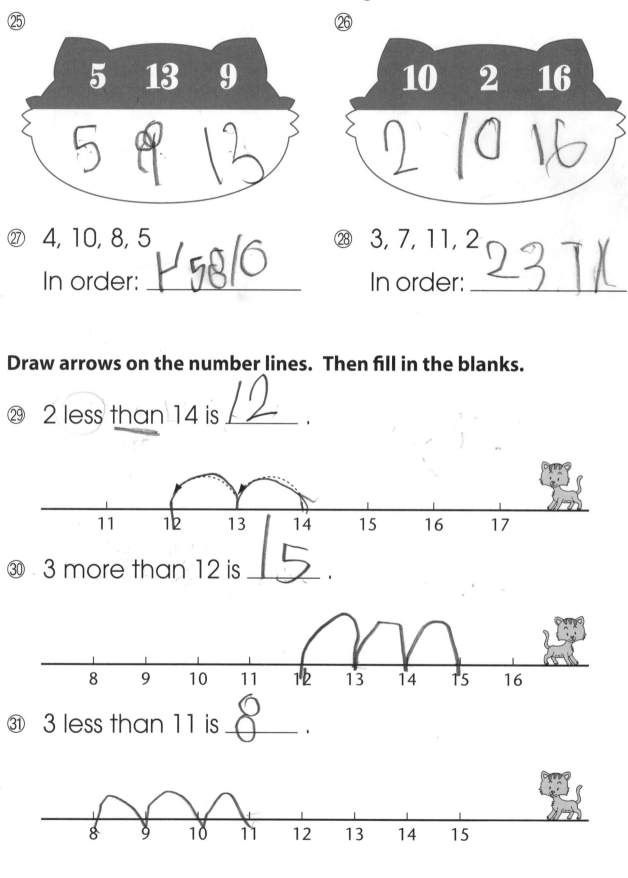

11   12   13   14   15   16   17

㉚ 3 more than 12 is _15_ .

8   9   10   11   12   13   14   15   16

㉛ 3 less than 11 is _8_ .

8   9   10   11   12   13   14   15

10

There are two ways to tell whether a number is **even** or **odd**.

- **By doing**

  Circle every two items. If there are no items left, the number is even; otherwise, it is odd.

- **By looking**

  Even number: a number ending in 0, 2, 4, 6, or 8

  Odd number: a number ending in 1, 3, 5, 7, or 9

← left

9 is an **odd** number.

14 ← ending in 4

14 is an **even** number.

Draw the correct number of dots to match each number. Then circle ◯ every two dots and tell whether the number is odd or even.

③②

13

13 is an _Odd_ number.

③③

12

12 is an ~~EVEN~~ number.

Look at the ending of each number. Then colour the even numbers yellow and the odd numbers red.

③④

9

3

10

6

8

20

14

18

15

Numbers 21 to 100

- Recognize the numbers from 21 to 100.
- Understand the place value of each digit in a 2-digit number.
- Compare numbers.
- Tell whether a given number is an even or odd number.

2 tens and 7 ones is 27.

Count and write the numbers.

①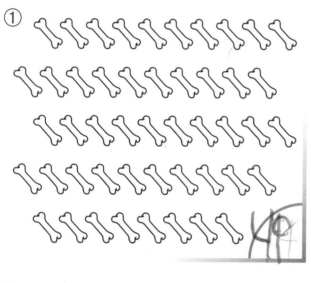

②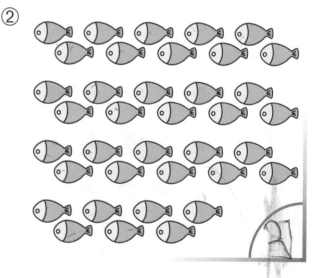

③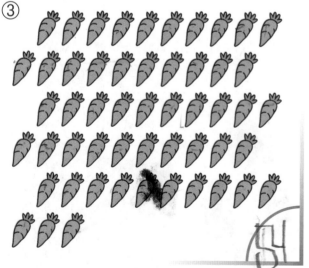

④

Complete the hundreds chart.

⑤

1	2	3	4	5	6	7	8	⑨	10
10	12	13	14	15	16	17	18	19	20
21	22	23	24	25	26	27	28	29	30
31	32	33	34	35	36	37	38	39	40
41	42	43	44	45	46	47	48	49	50
	53				56	57		59	60
61			64	65			68	69	
71		73		75	76			79	
	82	83			86	87			90
	92	93		95		97			100

9 ✓

Write the number that comes after.

⑥ 56 _____   ⑦ 72 _____   ⑧ 89 _____

Write the number that comes before.

⑨ _____ 94   ⑩ _____ 67   ⑪ _____ 40

Fill in the missing numbers.

⑫ 64 65 _____ _____ 68 69 _____ _____ 72

⑬ 88 89 _____ 91 _____ _____ 94 _____ 96

⑭ 44   43   ⎯   41   ⎯   ⎯   ⎯   37

Count and write the numbers.

⑮

Tens	Ones

= _____ tens and _____ ones

= _____ + _____

⑯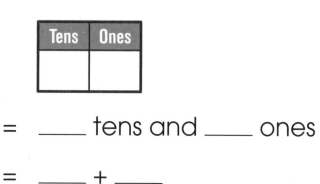

Tens	Ones

= _____ tens and _____ ones

= _____ + _____

Fill in the blanks.

⑰ 65 = _____ tens and _____ ones

⑱ 15 = _____ + 5

⑲ 38 = _____ tens and _____ ones

⑳ 46 = 40 + _____

㉑ 97 = _____ tens and _____ ones

㉒ 87 = _____ + _____

㉓ _____ = 5 tens and 3 ones

㉔ _____ = 30 + 4

㉕ _____ = 4 tens and 9 ones

㉖ _____ = 60 + 1

Colour the greater number in each pair.

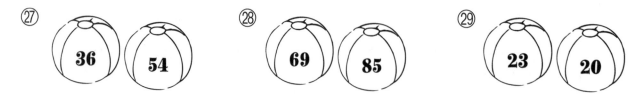

㉗ 36 54

㉘ 69 85

㉙ 23 20

Odd or even numbers:

If the digit in the ones place of a number is

- 1, 3, 5, 7, or 9, it is an **odd** number.
- 2, 4, 6, 8, or 0, it is an **even** number.

e.g.   45   96
       ↑   ↑
   odd number   even number

45 is an odd number and 96 is an even number.

Fill in the blanks with the help of the number lines.

㉚ 3 less than 91 is _88_.

㉛ 4 more than 27 is _31_.

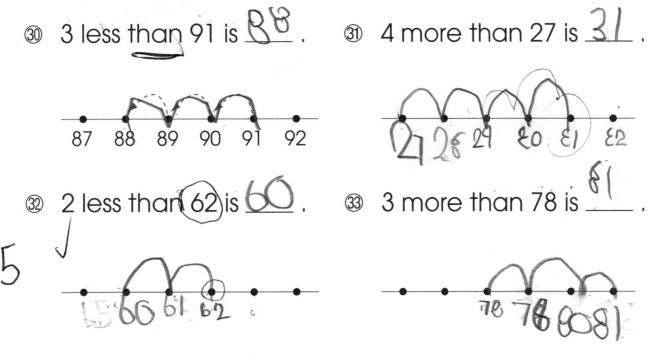

㉜ 2 less than 62 is _60_.

㉝ 3 more than 78 is _81_.

5 ✓

Look at the numbers on the bone. Answer the questions.

㉞ How many even numbers are there? What are they?

_5_ ; _70, 54, 16, 78, 82_

㉟ Which odd number is greater than 80?

_91_

70,

Counting by 1's, 2's, 5's, and 10's

- Count forward by 1's, 2's, 5's, and 10's.
- Count backward by 1's, 2's, and 5's from 20.
- Find out the best way to do counting.

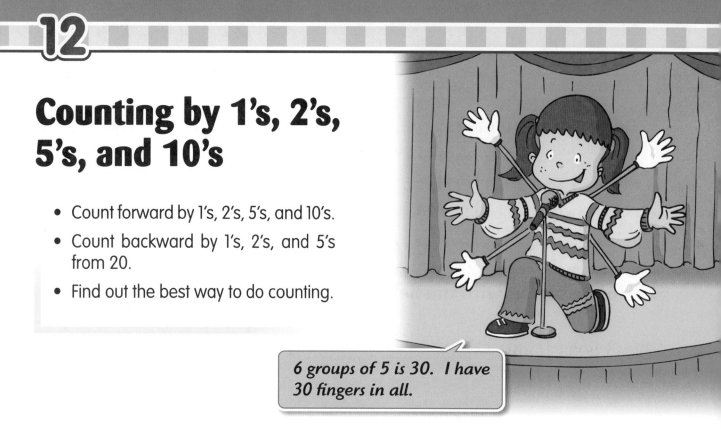

6 groups of 5 is 30. I have 30 fingers in all.

Fill in the missing numbers.

① 85 86 ____ ____ 89 ____ ____ ____ 93 94

② 12 11 ____ ____ 8 ____ ____ 5 ____ 3

③ 19 18 ____ 16 ____ ____ 13 ____ ____ 10

④ 64 65 ____ ____ 68 ____ ____ ____ 72 73

Read what the bees say. Write the numbers.

⑤ *Count forward by 1's from 47 to 58.*

_____

⑥ *Count backward by 1's from 16 to 6.*

_____

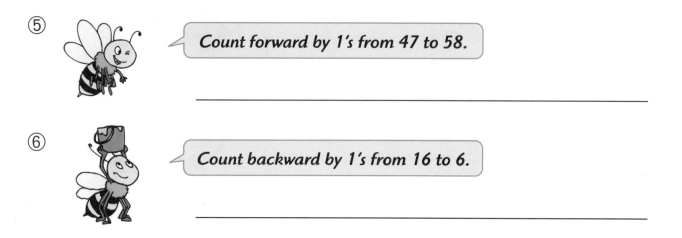

Circle ◯ the objects in groups of 2. Then fill in the blanks.

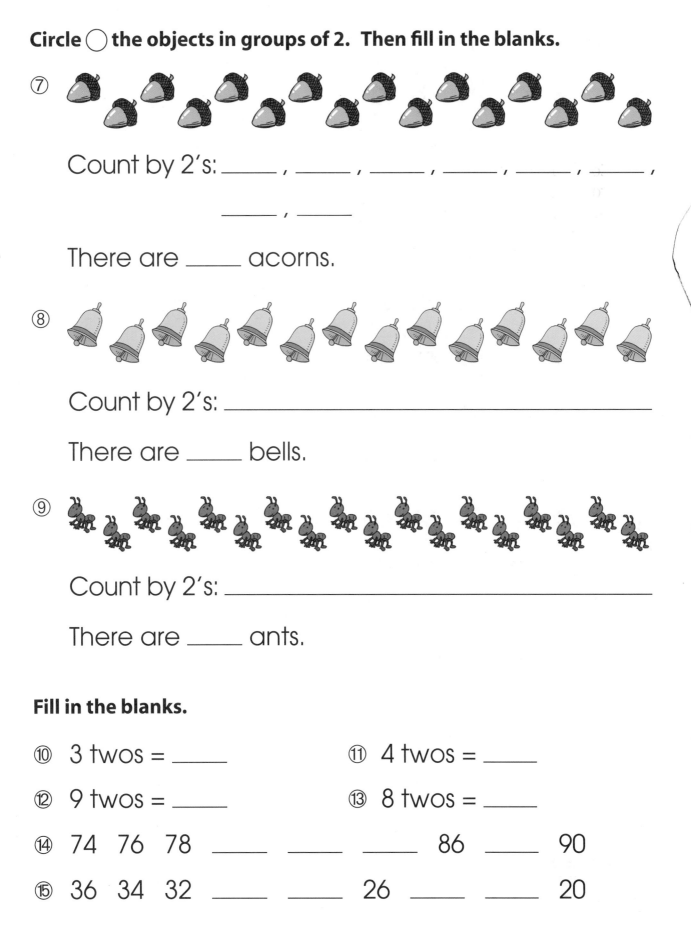

⑦

Count by 2's: _____ , _____ , _____ , _____ , _____ , _____ ,

_____ , _____

There are _____ acorns.

⑧

Count by 2's: _____

There are _____ bells.

⑨

Count by 2's: _____

There are _____ ants.

Fill in the blanks.

⑩ 3 twos = _____   ⑪ 4 twos = _____

⑫ 9 twos = _____   ⑬ 8 twos = _____

⑭ 74 76 78 _____ _____ _____ 86 _____ 90

⑮ 36 34 32 _____ _____ 26 _____ 20

Fill in the blanks with the help of the picture.

⑯

a. 1 five is _____ .

b. 2 fives are _____ .

c. 3 fives are _____ .

d. 4 fives are _____ .

e. 5 fives are _____ .

f. 6 fives are _____ .

g. 7 fives are _____ .

h. 8 fives are _____ .

i. 9 fives are _____ .

j. 10 fives are _____ .

Fill in the missing numbers.

⑰ 25 30 _____ 40 _____ _____ 55 _____

⑱ 60 65 _____ _____ 80 _____ 90 _____

⑲ 80 75 _____ _____ 55 _____ 45

⑳ 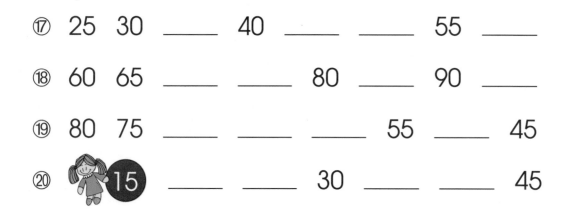 15 _____ _____ 30 _____ _____ 45

Circle ◯ the objects in groups of 10. Count and write the numbers.

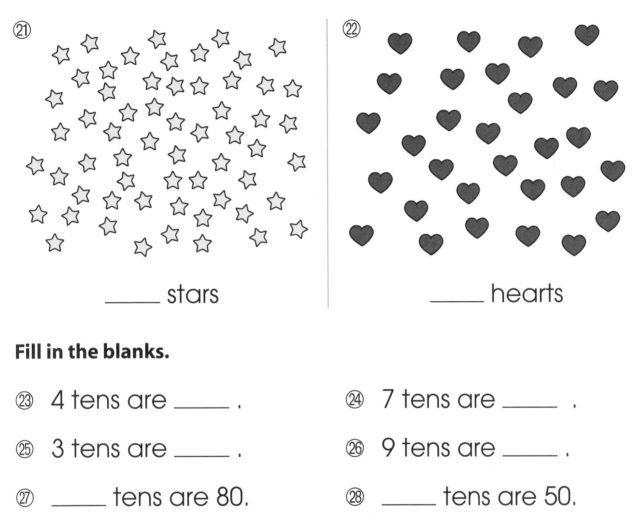

㉑ _____ stars

㉒ _____ hearts

Fill in the blanks.

㉓ 4 tens are _____ .

㉔ 7 tens are _____ .

㉕ 3 tens are _____ .

㉖ 9 tens are _____ .

㉗ _____ tens are 80.

㉘ _____ tens are 50.

Circle ◯ the correct words. Then write the numbers.

㉙

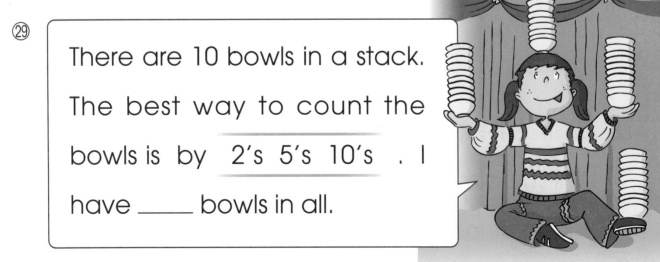

There are 10 bowls in a stack. The best way to count the bowls is by 2's 5's 10's . I have _____ bowls in all.

Money

- Identify the names and state the values of coins.
- Compare and order coins by size and value.
- Write money amounts to 20¢.
- Add and subtract money amounts to 10¢.

Draw lines to match the coins with their names. Then write the values of the coins.

①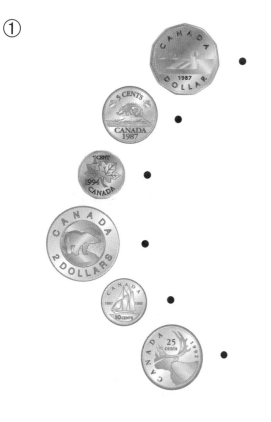

- Toonie ; $ _____
- Loonie ; $ _____
- Quarter ; _____ ¢
- Dime ; _____ ¢
- Nickel ; _____ ¢
- Penny ; _____ ¢

Look at the coins above again. Answer the questions.

② Which coin is the biggest in size? _____

③ Which coin is the smallest in size? _____

Circle ◯ the coin with a greater value in each pair.

Put the coins in order from the one with the greatest value to the one with the least. Write the letters.

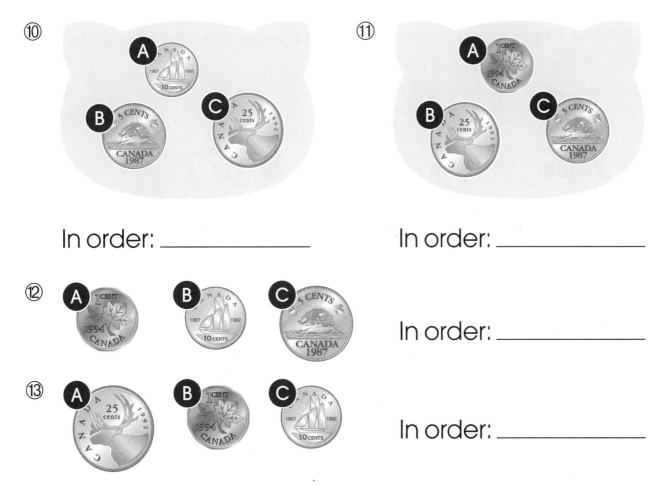

⑩ In order: _____

⑪ In order: _____

⑫ In order: _____

⑬ In order: _____

Find the value of each group of coins.

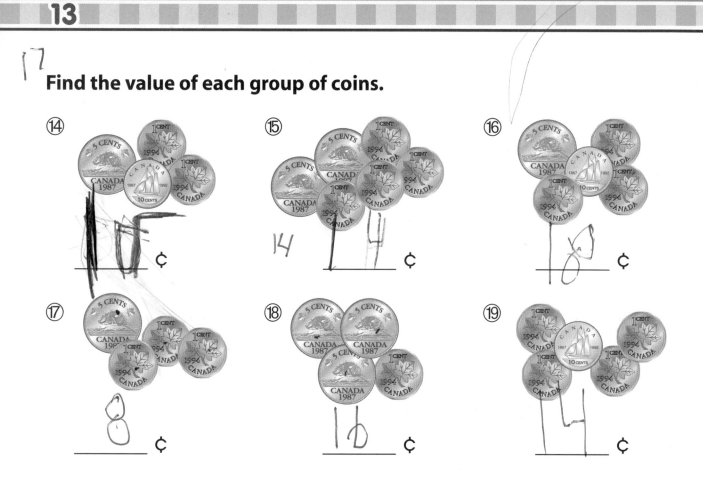

⑭ _____ ¢

⑮ _____ ¢

⑯ _____ ¢

⑰ _____ ¢

⑱ _____ ¢

⑲ _____ ¢

Check ✔ the correct number of coins to show the cost of each toy.

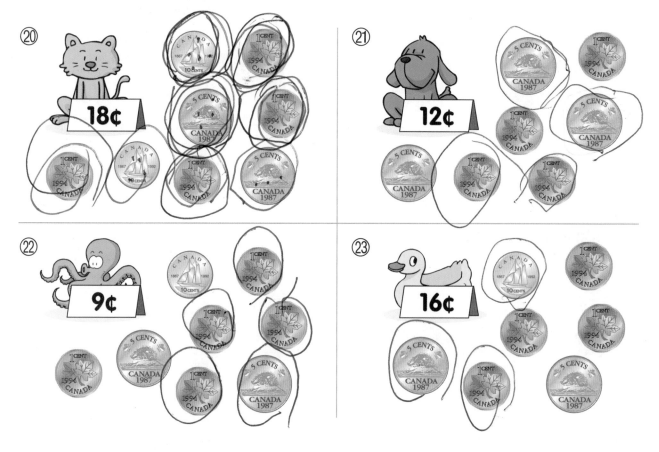

⑳ 18¢

㉑ 12¢

㉒ 9¢

㉓ 16¢

Use addition to find the total and subtraction to find the change.

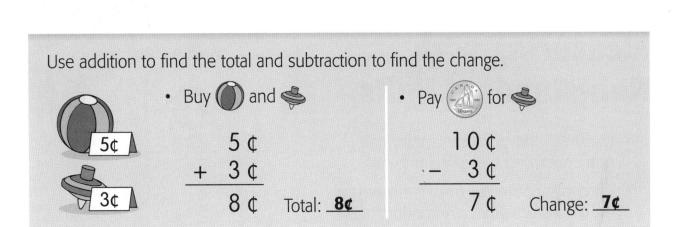

- Buy  and

	5 ¢
+	3 ¢
	8 ¢

Total: **8¢**

- Pay for

	1 0 ¢
−	3 ¢
	7 ¢

Change: **7¢**

Look at the pictures.   Answer the questions.

   Happy Birthday   **5¢**

 **4¢**

3¢

8¢

㉔ Tom wants to buy a bear and a card for his mom. How much does he need to pay?

_____9__ ¢

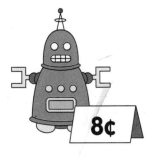

	4 ¢
+	5 ¢
	9 ¢

㉕ How much more does a robot cost than a butterfly?

_____5__ ¢

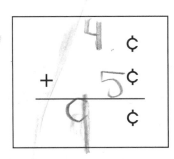

8 5¢

㉖

> If I pay for a robot with a dime, what is my change?

10 ¢
8
2
2

_____2__ ¢

Measuring with Non-standard Units

- Measure and describe length, height, and area using non-standard units.
- Compare and order objects based on the measurement in non-standard units.

How many pencils or nails long is each item?   Count and write the numbers to complete the sentences.

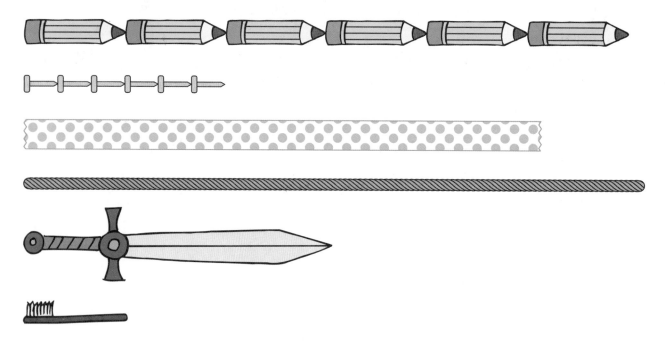

① The ribbon is about _____ pencils or _____ nails long.

② The rope is about _____ pencils or _____ nails long.

③ The sword is about _____ pencils or _____ nails long.

④ The toothbrush is about _____ pencil or _____ nails long.

Draw pictures to match the descriptions.

⑤ A fish that is 3 pencils long and a rope that is a bit longer than 4 pencils

⑥ A sandwich that is 1 paper clip thick and a box that is a bit thinner than 2 paper clips

⑦ A tree that is 3 floors high and a building that is 1 floor taller than the given building

Which is the better unit for each measurement? Circle ⭘ the correct answer.

⑧ The length of a long aisle: combs   belts

⑨ The height of a coffee table: straws   screws

14

What is the distance between the objects? Write the numbers on the lines and circle ◯ the correct pictures and numbers.

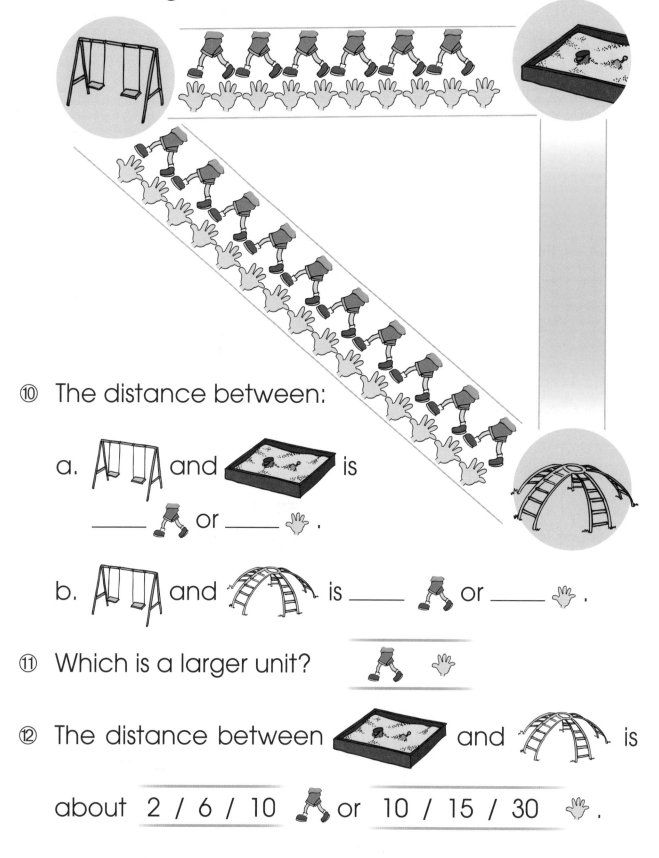

⑩ The distance between:

a. [swing] and [sandbox] is

_____ [foot] or _____ [hand] .

b. [swing] and [dome climber] is _____ [foot] or _____ [hand] .

⑪ Which is a larger unit?   [foot]   [hand]

⑫ The distance between [sandbox] and [dome climber] is

about 2 / 6 / 10 [foot] or 10 / 15 / 30 [hand] .

Look at the pictures. Find the number of stickers needed to cover each picture and circle ◯ the correct answer.

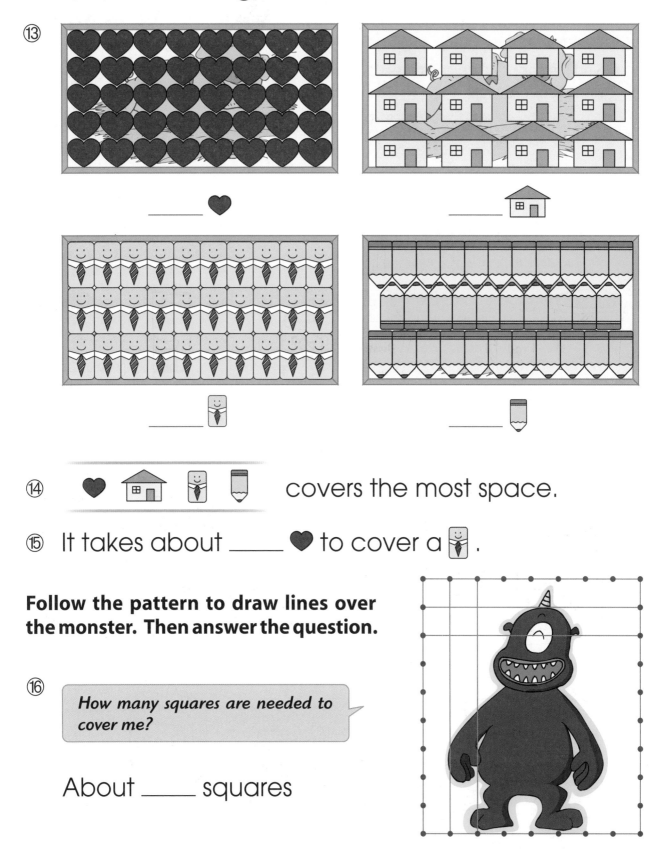

⑬

_____ ♥

_____ 🏠

_____ 👔

_____ ✏️

⑭ ♥ 🏠 👔 ✏️ covers the most space.
_____

⑮ It takes about _____ ♥ to cover a 👔.

Follow the pattern to draw lines over the monster. Then answer the question.

⑯

How many squares are needed to cover me?

About _____ squares

15

Capacity

- Estimate and compare capacities of containers.
- Find the capacity of a container using non-standard units.

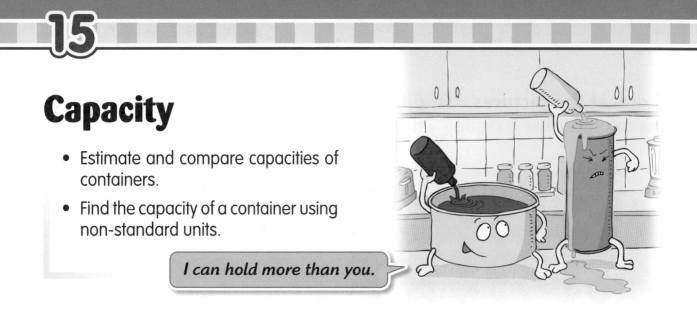

I can hold more than you.

Colour the one with a greater capacity.

① ② ③

Dressing POP

Chips

Colour the one with the greatest capacity.

④ ⑤

⑥ ⑦

YOGOURT

DETERGENT

SOAP

Look at the pictures.   Circle ◯ the correct answers to complete the sentences.

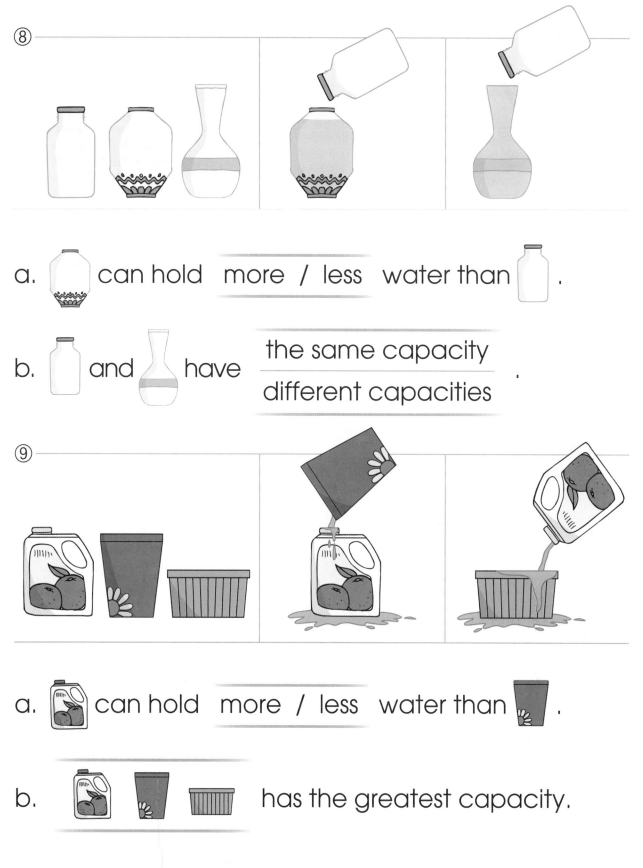

⑧

a. ⬜ can hold more / less water than ⬜ .

b. ⬜ and ⬜ have the same capacity / different capacities .

⑨

a. ⬜ can hold more / less water than ⬜ .

b. ⬜ ⬜ ⬜ has the greatest capacity.

See how many cups or pails are needed to hold the water in each container. Write the numbers. Then complete the sentences.

⑩

a. [jar] fills ＿＿ cups and [jug] fills ＿＿ cups.

b. [jug] can hold ＿＿ more cups of water than [jar] .

⑪

a. [box] fills ＿＿ pails.

b. [tub] fills ＿＿ [box] and ＿＿ pails.

c. [tub] can hold more / less water than [box] .

d. [tub] can hold ＿＿ pails of water.

Choose the most appropriate thing to measure the capacity of the container on the left. Check ✔ the letters.

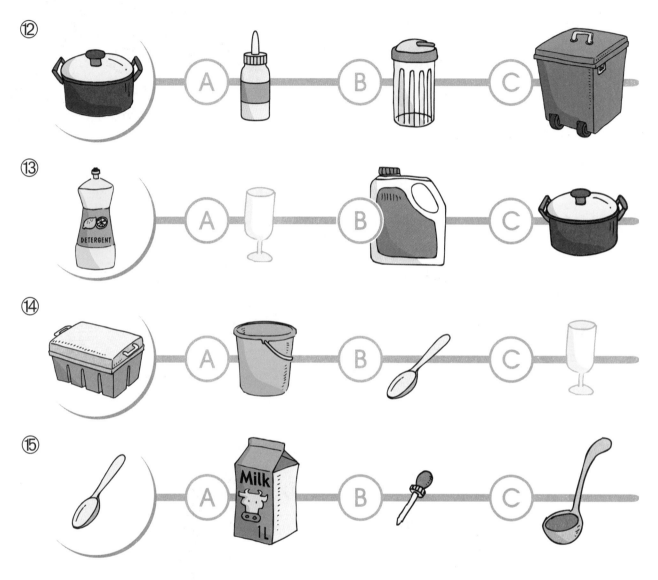

Circle ◯ the correct number to complete what the can says.

⑯

It takes 6 boxes of juice to fill me up. If my brother can hold 2 more boxes, my brother can hold   4 / 2 / 8   boxes of juice.

Mass

- Compare and order masses of objects.
- Describe masses of objects using relative terms.
- Estimate, measure, and record masses of objects using non-standard units.

You're heavier.

Check ✔ the heavier thing in each pair.

①

②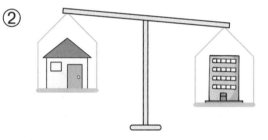

Put the things in order from lightest to heaviest. Write 1 to 3.

③

④

⑤

Draw lines to match the things that are about the same mass.

⑥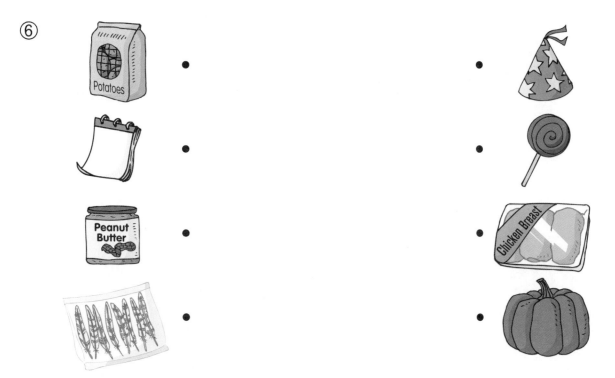

Look at the pictures. Fill in the blanks with "lighter" or "heavier".

⑦

a. A pineapple is _____ than an apple.

b. A cherry is _____ than an apple.

⑧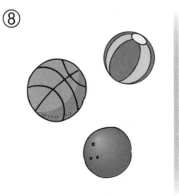

a. A basketball is _____ than a beach ball.

b. A basketball is _____ than a bowling ball.

How many blocks are needed to balance each thing? Count and write the number. Then answer the questions.

⑨

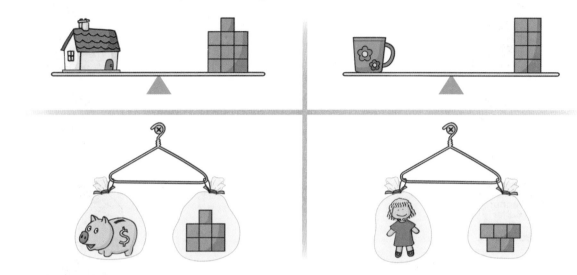

a. The house has the same weight as ____ blocks.

b. The mug has the same weight as ____ blocks.

c. The piggy bank has the same weight as ____ blocks.

d. The doll has the same weight as ____ blocks.

⑩ Which thing is the heaviest?   _____

⑪ Which thing is the lightest?   _____

Look at the pictures above again. Then draw the correct number of blocks on the correct side to balance the objects.

⑫

Look at the pictures. Fill in the blanks.

⑬ The car has the same weight as ____ blocks.

⑭ The figurine has the same weight as ____ blocks.

⑮ The snowman has the same weight as ____ blocks.

⑯ ____ figurines are needed to balance the car.

⑰ It takes ____ car(s) and ____ figurine(s) to balance the snowman.

Read what the mouse says. Help him draw the correct number of fish to balance the cat.

⑱

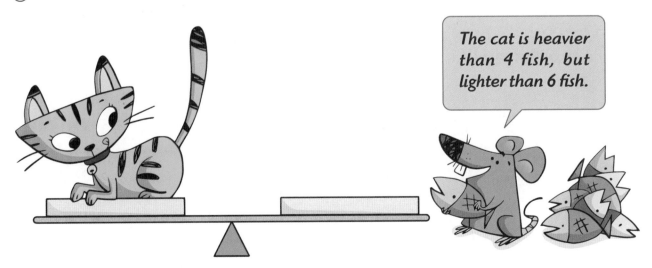

The cat is heavier than 4 fish, but lighter than 6 fish.

2-D Shapes

- Identify and describe common 2-D shapes such as circles and squares.
- Tell the number of sides and corners of 2-D shapes.

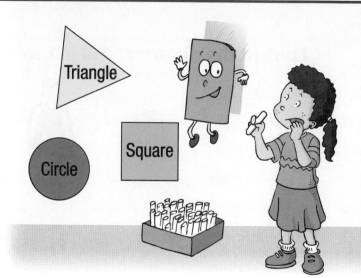

Draw lines to match the shapes with their names.

①

Circle   •

Hexagon   •

Pentagon   •

Rectangle   •

Square   •

Triangle   •

Trace the dotted lines. Then name the shapes.

②

③

④

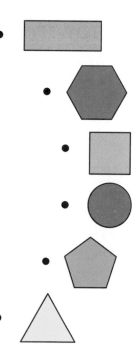

_____   _____   _____

Trace each shape on the left on a piece of tracing paper. Then cut it out and compare it with each of the coloured shapes on the right. Describe the shapes.

wider   narrower   taller   shorter
bigger   smaller   the same

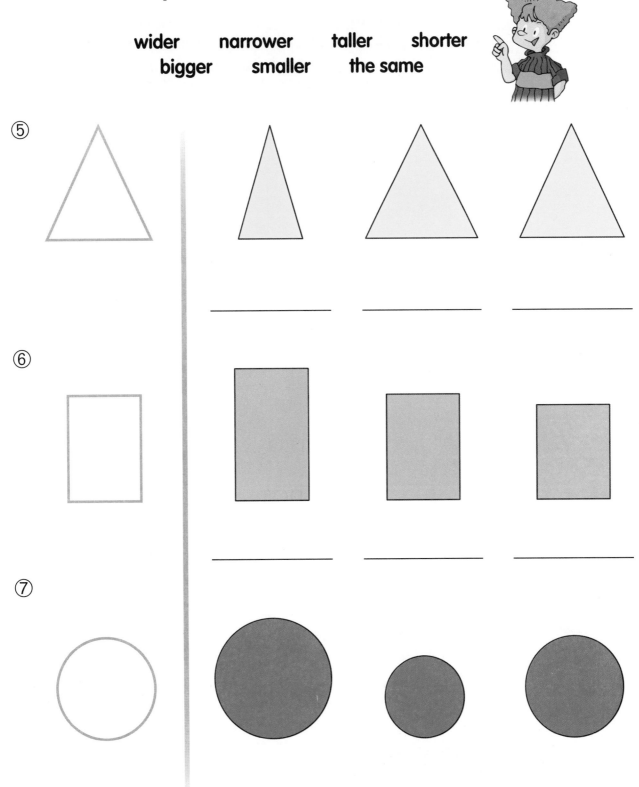

⑤

⑥

⑦

Join the dots in order. Then name the shapes and write the numbers.

⑧

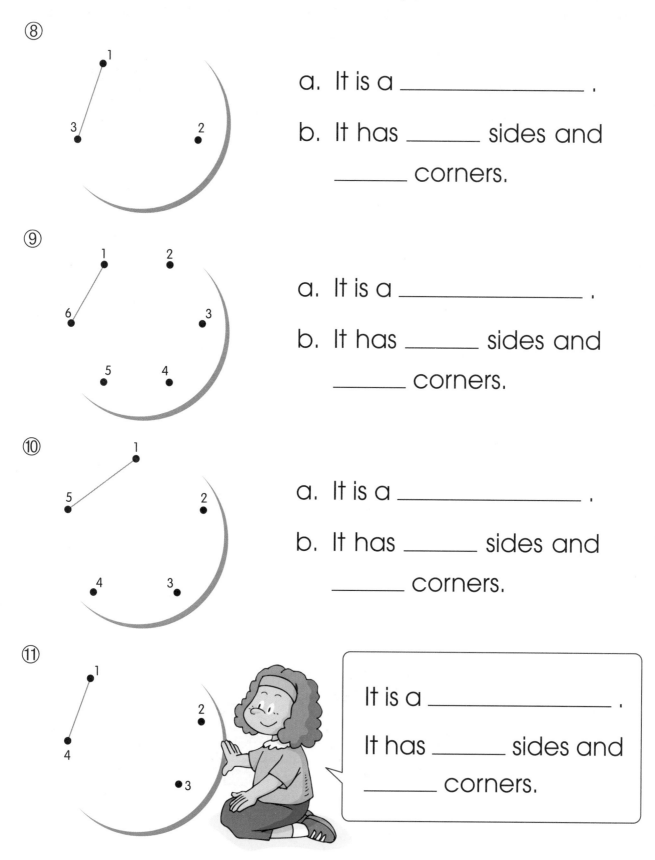

a. It is a _____ .

b. It has _____ sides and
_____ corners.

⑨

a. It is a _____ .

b. It has _____ sides and
_____ corners.

⑩

a. It is a _____ .

b. It has _____ sides and
_____ corners.

⑪

It is a _____ .

It has _____ sides and
_____ corners.

Colour the pentagons red and the hexagons yellow.

⑫

Read what the girl says. Help her draw the robot.

⑬

My robot's head is a rectangle. His eyes are pentagons and his nose is a hexagon. His ears are triangles and his mouth is a circle.

More about Shapes

- Identify shapes in a given design.
- Identify and complete symmetrical shapes.
- Use fractions to describe parts of a whole.

We are all symmetrical.

Trace the dotted lines. Then write the names of the shapes that you can see in each design.

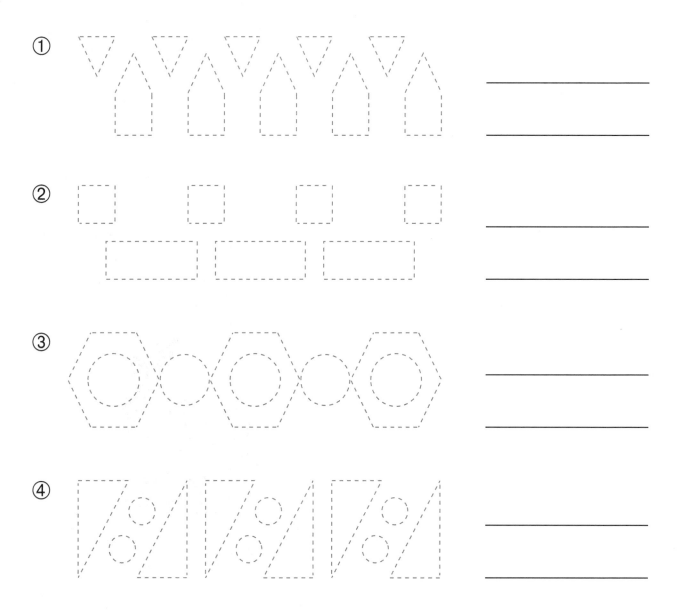

① _____

_____

② _____

_____

③ _____

_____

④ _____

_____

Colour the symmetrical pictures.

⑤

Draw the missing parts to make each picture symmetrical.

⑥

Trace the dotted lines and colour one part of each shape. Then tell how much is coloured.

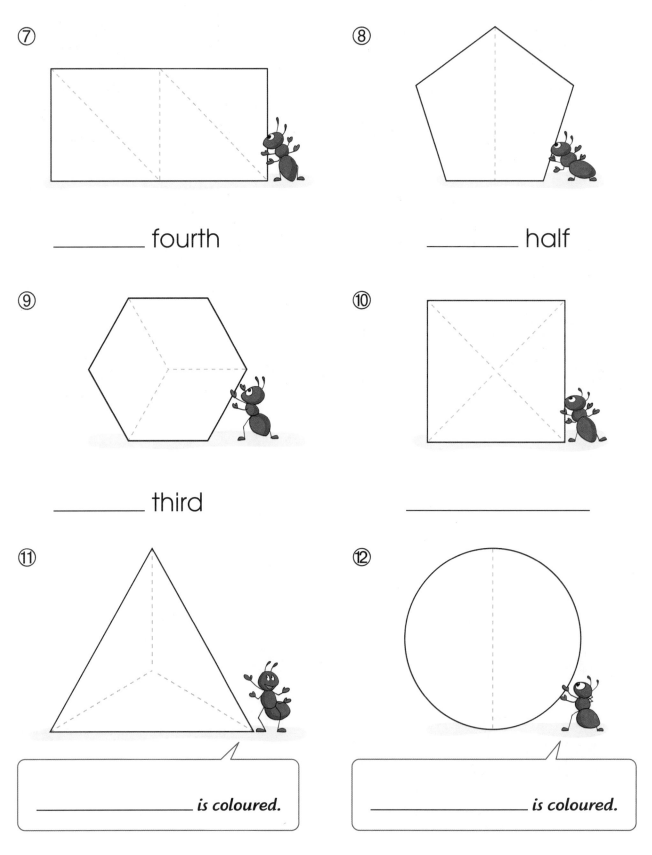

⑦ _____ fourth

⑧ _____ half

⑨ _____ third

⑩ _____

⑪ _____ *is coloured.*

⑫ _____ *is coloured.*

Look at the pictures. Fill in the blanks.

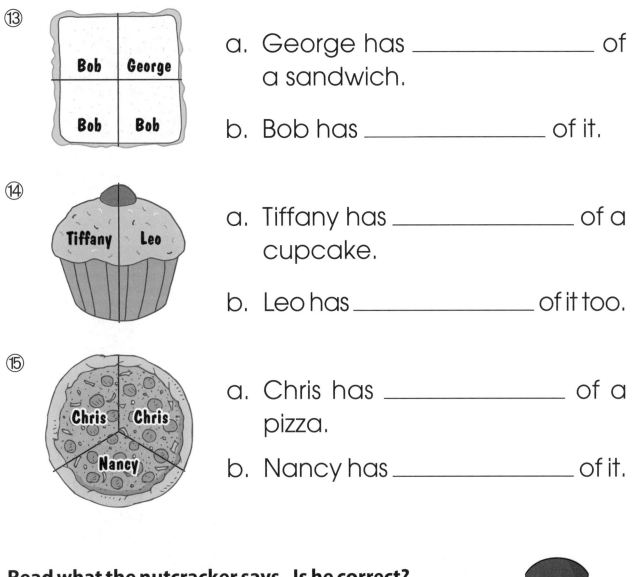

⑬

a. George has _____ of a sandwich.

b. Bob has _____ of it.

⑭

a. Tiffany has _____ of a cupcake.

b. Leo has _____ of it too.

⑮

a. Chris has _____ of a pizza.

b. Nancy has _____ of it.

Read what the nutcracker says. Is he correct? Explain.

⑯

One quarter of my sword is shaded.

_____

_____

_____

3-D Solids

- Identify and complete common 3-D solids.
- Identify the faces of 3-D solids.
- Describe similarities and differences between common objects and 3-D solids.

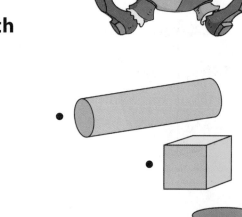

Do I look like a sphere?

Draw lines to match the solids with their names.

①

Cone •

Cube •

Cylinder •

Prism •

Sphere •

Trace the dotted lines to complete the solids. Then name them.

②

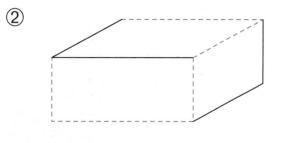

_____

③

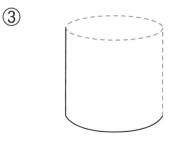

_____

What solid does each object look like? Write the name of the 3-D solid. Then draw one thing which has the same shape as the one given.

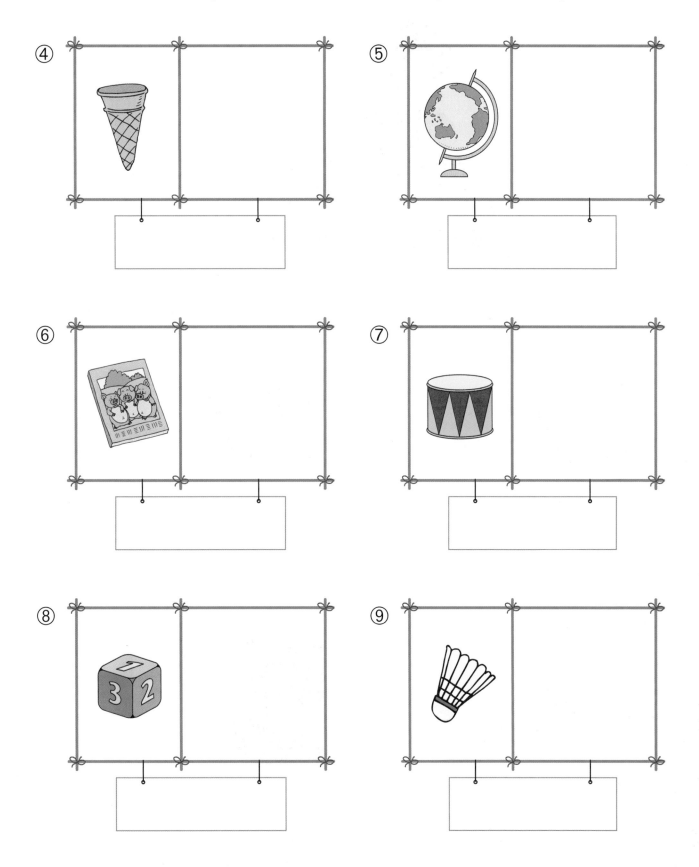

④

⑤

⑥

⑦

⑧

⑨

See how Bruce traces the 3-D solids. Draw and name the traced faces.

⑩

The traced face is in the shape of a _____ .

⑪ _____

⑫ _____

⑬ _____

⑭ _____

Compare everyday objects and 3-D solids to find their **differences** and **similarities**.

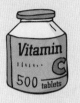

The bottle looks like a cylinder, except that it gets thinner at the top.

A sphere can **roll**.

A cube can **slide**.

What 3-D solids do these objects look like?   Name the solids and describe them.

⑮   It looks like a _____ , _____

_____ .

⑯   It looks like a _____ , _____

_____ .

⑰   It looks like a _____ , _____

_____ .

Read what the clown says. Help him colour the solids.

⑱   *Colour the solids that can both roll and slide.*

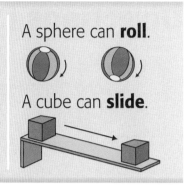

Directions (1)

- Use words such as "in front of", "behind", "left", and "right" to describe positions.
- Complete a picture to show the position of things.

I'm on your right, Mom.

And I'm on your left.

Look at the picture. Circle ⟡ the correct answers.

① Alex is in front of   Judy / Tom / Eric   .

② Judy is behind   Bill / Alex / Sue   .

③ Eric is   in front of / behind   Sue.

④ Bill is   in front of / behind   Tom.

⑤ There are   2 / 3 / 5   children in front of Judy.

⑥ There are   4 / 3 / 2   children behind Alex.

Colour the correct pictures to match the sentences. Then fill in the blanks with "in front of" or "behind" to describe the coloured pictures.

⑦ The dog is in front of the pet carrier and the cat is behind the pet carrier.

a.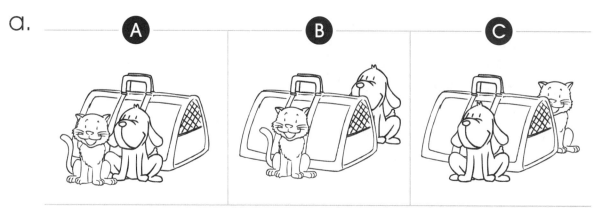

b. The pet carrier is _____ the cat.

c. The pet carrier is _____ the dog.

⑧ The house is in front of the cat and the tree is behind the cat.

a.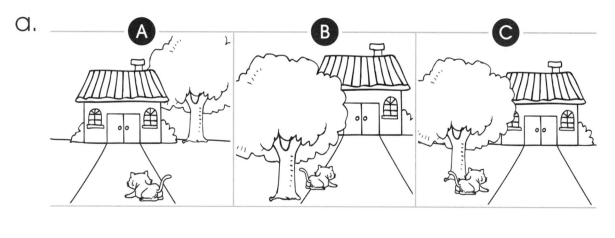

b. The cat is _____ the house.

c. The tree is _____ the house.

Look at the pictures. Fill in the blanks with "left" or "right".

⑨

a. The two-eyed alien is on the _____ of Tom.

b. The one-eyed alien is on the _____ of Tom.

c. The one-eyed alien has a stethoscope in his _____ hand.

⑩ a. Ray has an umbrella in his _____ hand.

b. The cactus is on the _____ of Ray.

c. Ray is on the _____ of the cactus.

Complete the picture.

⑪ Draw two carrots on the left of the small rabbit and one apple on the left of the big rabbit.

Read the clues to find the names of the girls. Write the names in the boxes and fill in the blanks with "in front of", "behind", "left", or "right".

⑫　• Mabel and Cindy are on the right of Tammy.
　　• Sue is on the left of Tammy.
　　• Cindy is on the right of Mabel.

⑬　There are many shapes _____ the girls.

⑭　There is a window _____ one of the girls.

⑮　Tammy is on the _____ of Mabel.

⑯　Cindy is on the _____ of Sue.

Look at the picture. Complete the sentences.

⑰　The girl is _____ the boy.

⑱　The boy has a balloon in his _____ hand.

⑲　The girl has a lollipop in her _____ hand.

Directions (2)

- Use words such as "inside", "outside", "over", and "under" to describe positions.
- Complete a picture to show the positions of things.

Although I'm inside a cage under you, you can't reach me.

Look at the pictures.   Circle ◯ the correct answers.

①

a. Amy is   inside / outside   the room.

b. A cat is   inside / outside   the room.

②

a. A bee is inside / outside the jar.

b. A butterfly is inside / outside the jar.

③

a. Mom is going inside / outside .

b. Brother Ant and Sister Ant are playing ball inside / outside .

Look at the picture. Fill in the blanks with "over" or "under". Then draw things to complete the picture.

④

a. Lucy is _____ the roof.

b. A toy helicopter is flying _____ the roof.

c. A pail is _____ the bridge.

d. Louis is _____ the umbrella.

e. A dog is crawling _____ the stairs.

f. A ball is thrown _____ the bridge.

g. Draw a bird flying under the clouds.

h. Draw a rainbow over the clouds.

Read each sentence. Colour the correct picture. Then fill in the blank to give one more description of the coloured picture.

⑤ A cat is under the table and it is outside the box.

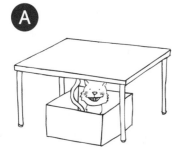

The box is _____ the table.

⑥ A fly is flying over the food dome and a cake is inside the dome.

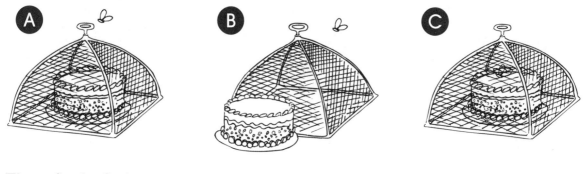

The fly is flying _____ the cake.

⑦ The outside of the box has stripes and a frog is jumping over the box.

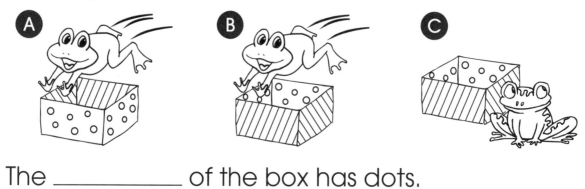

The _____ of the box has dots.

Look at the picture. Fill in the blanks.

⑧ There are 3 balls _____ the basket.

⑨ The fairy is flying _____ the lion.

⑩ There is a ball _____ the lion's left paw.

⑪ The mouse has his hands _____ his head.

⑫ The lion is _____ the cage.

Help the mouse write two sentences with the given words to describe the picture above.

⑬ stars, over: _____

_____

⑭ mouse, inside: _____

_____

Temperatures

- Recognize the names and characteristics of the four seasons.
- Use simple words to describe different weather conditions.
- Read and record temperatures in degrees Celsius (°C) with a thermometer.

Four-Season Show

Match the pictures with the seasons. Write the letters.

①

Spring: _____ Summer: _____

Fall: _____ Winter: _____

Which season does each picture show? Write the name of the season. Then put the pictures in order starting with spring. Write 1 to 4.

②

a.   b.

c.   d.

Fill in the blanks with the given words and draw pictures in the boxes to complete the "Weather Facts".

hottest	coldest	warm
cold	snowy	sunny

Weather Facts

③

Spring: _____ , cool to _____

Summer: _____ , the _____ season

Fall: cool to _____

Winter: _____ , the _____ season

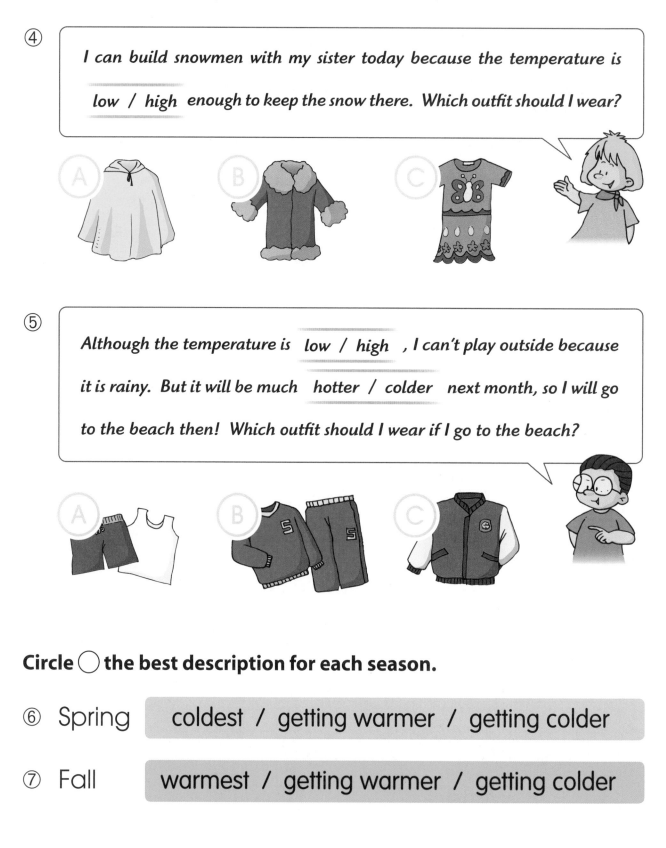

Circle ◯ the correct words to complete what the children say. Then help the children check ✔ the correct clothing.

④ I can build snowmen with my sister today because the temperature is low / high enough to keep the snow there. Which outfit should I wear?

⑤ Although the temperature is low / high , I can't play outside because it is rainy. But it will be much hotter / colder next month, so I will go to the beach then! Which outfit should I wear if I go to the beach?

Circle ◯ the best description for each season.

⑥ Spring — coldest / getting warmer / getting colder

⑦ Fall — warmest / getting warmer / getting colder

Temperature is measured in **degrees Celsius (°C)**.

When the temperature gets higher, the weather gets hotter.

25°C

5°C

Record the temperatures. Then circle ◯ the best word to describe each temperature.

⑧ ____°C

cold

mild

hot

⑨ ____°C

cold

mild

hot

⑩ ____°C

cold

mild

hot

⑪ ____°C

cold

mild

hot

Read what the girl says. Help her colour the thermometer to show the temperature.

⑫ *Yesterday's temperature was 23°C. Today's temperature is 4°C higher than that of yesterday. What is today's temperature?*

_____°C

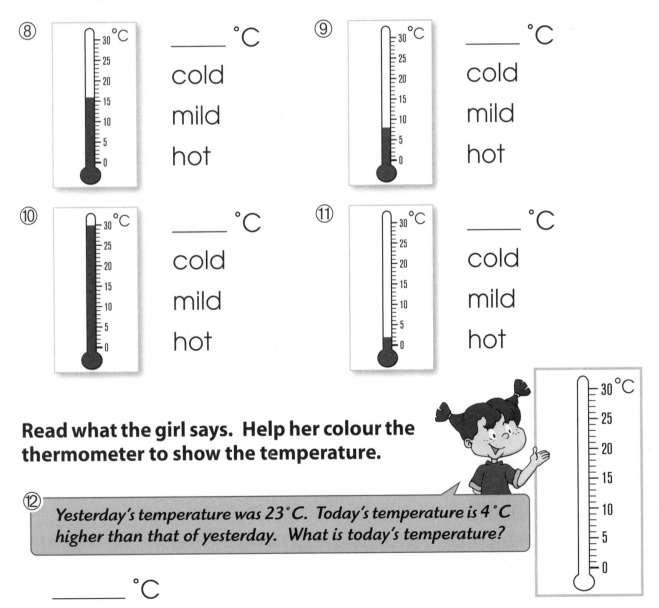

23

Days, Weeks, Months, and Time

- Name the days of the week.
- Put the months of the year in order and read the date on a calendar.
- Read and write time to the hour and half-hour.
- Draw clock hands to show time.

Half past 7

See what Eric will do next week. Help him answer the questions.

SUN   MON and TUE   WED   THU   FRI   SAT

① Eric will play ball on _____ .

② On _____ and _____ , Eric will play computer games.

③ On how many days will Eric read books?   _____ days

④ On which day of the week will he have two things to do?   _____

⑤ What will he do on the first day of the week?   _____

⑥ How many days are there in a week?   _____ days

Put the months in the correct order starting with January. Write 1 – 12.

⑦ _____ May   _____ September   _____ July

_____ June   _____ October   _____ February

_____ March   _____ December   _1_ January

_____ April   _____ November   _____ August

Fill in the missing information on Jill's calendar. Then answer the questions.

⑧

OCT ___ ___ ___ R   's Calendar

SUN	MON			THU		SAT
	1	2	3	(4)		6
7			10		12	13
🎂	15			18	19	
	22	23				27
28			🎃			

◯ Field Trip

⑨ The first day of this month is a _____ .

⑩ What is the date of Jill's field trip?   _____

⑪ When is the birthday of Jill's mom?   _____

⑫ Jill will buy a costume 2 days before
Halloween. What is the date?   _____

See what Nancy did yesterday. Help her write the times in 2 ways. Then put the pictures in the correct order.

⑬

A

half past _____

_____ : 30

B

_____

_____ : _____

C

_____

_____ : _____

D

_____

_____ : _____

⑭ In order: _____ , _____ , _____ , _____

Use "nearly" or "a little after" to write the times.

⑮

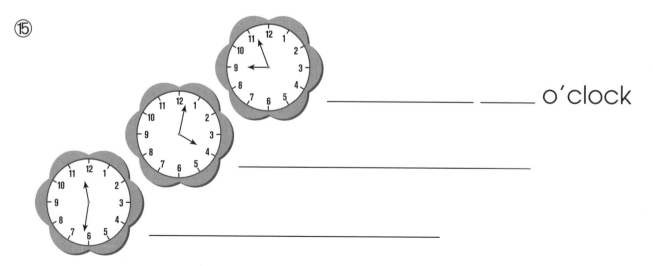

_____ _____ o'clock

_____

_____

The long hand is the **minute hand**. The short hand is the **hour hand**.

It is half past 8. The long hand points to 6 and the short one points to the middle of 8 and 9.

Draw the clock hands to show the times.

⑯ 9:00

⑰ 3:30

⑱ 10:30

⑲ 4:30

⑳ 7:00

㉑ 5:00

Help Cindy the Clock complete the clock face and draw the clock hands to show the time.

㉒ *It is a little after half past 3 right now.*

Patterns

- Identify the pattern of a group of things.
- Continue a pattern by drawing or colouring.
- Create a pattern with the given objects.
- Find patterns in a hundreds chart.

Can you see the pattern on my crown?

Put a check mark ✔ in the circle if each group of pictures follows a pattern; otherwise, put a cross ✘.

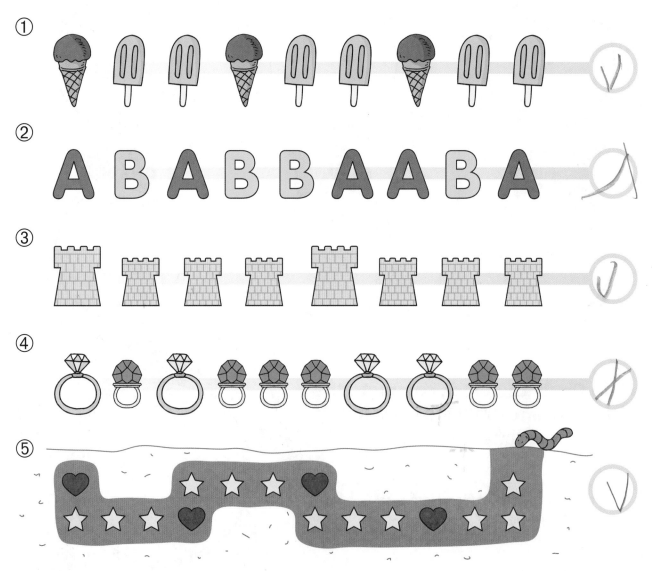

Draw the next two pictures.

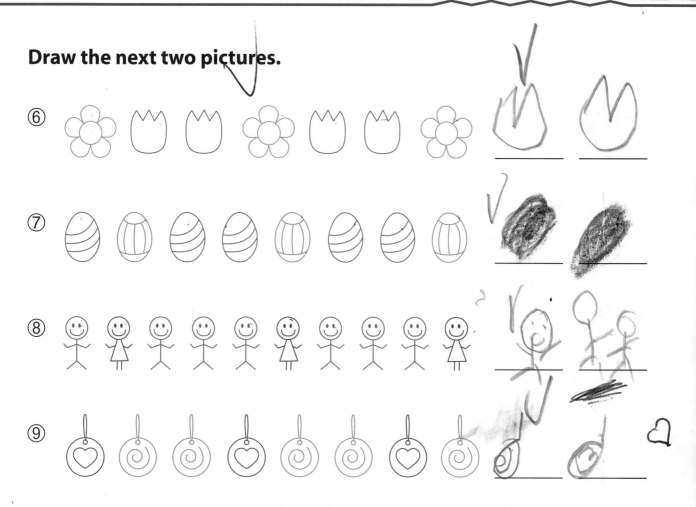

⑥

⑦

⑧

⑨

Cross out ✗ one picture in each group so that the pictures follow a pattern.

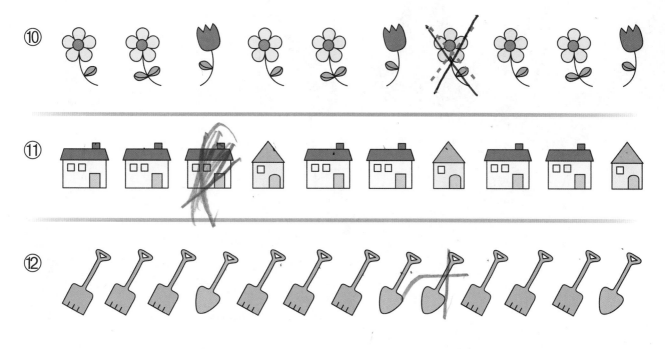

⑩

⑪

⑫

Draw the missing picture in each pattern. Then use each set of pictures to create a pattern different from the one above the line.

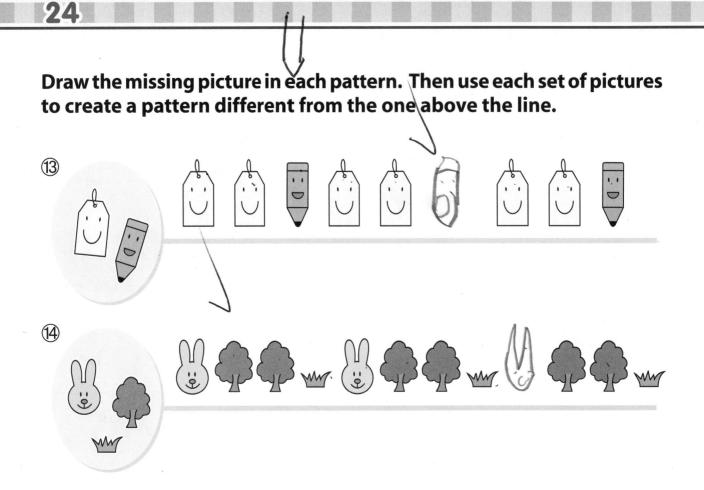

⑬

⑭

Trace the dotted lines to complete the patterns.

⑮

Hundreds chart:

a chart with 10 rows, 10 columns, and 100 boxes, each containing a number from 1 to 100 arranged in order

10 columns

1	2	3	4	5	6	7	8	9	10
11	12	13	14	15	16	17	18	19	20
21	22	23	24	25	26	27	28	29	30
31	32	33	34	35	36	37	38	39	40
41	42	43	44	45	46	47	48	49	50
51	52	53	54	55	56	57	58	59	60
61	62	63	64	65	66	67	68	69	70
71	72	73	74	75	76	77	78	79	80
81	82	83	84	85	86	97	88	89	90
91	92	93	94	95	96	97	98	99	100

10 rows

Fill in the missing numbers in the hundreds chart. Colour to continue the pattern of the coloured numbers. Then answer the question.

⑯

1	2	3	4	5	6	7	8	9	10
11	12	13	14					19	
21	22	23	24	25		27			
31	32	33	34						
41	42	43	44						
51	52	53	54	55		57			
61	62	63	64						70
71	72	73	74				78	79	
81	82	83	84		86	87			90
91	92	93	94	95					100

⑰

Look at the ones place of the coloured numbers. What pattern do you see?

Tens	Ones
2	5

_____

Organizing Data

- Organize objects into categories by sorting.
- Use a variety of recording methods to display data.

You really know how to organize things.

Healthful Food Junk Food

Sort the items in two ways. Count and write the numbers.

①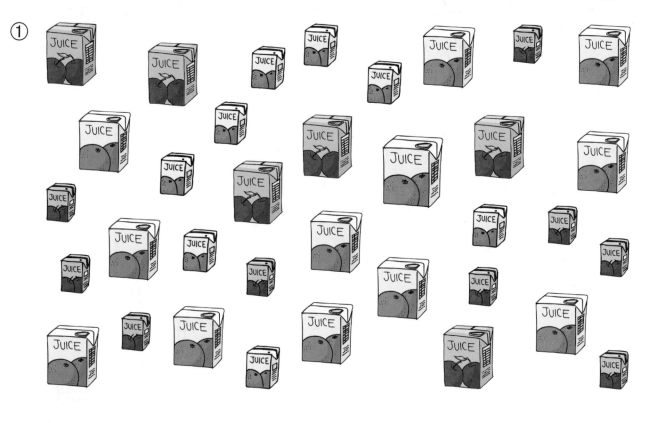

A **By flavour**	
Flavour	Number of boxes
Apple	
Orange	

B **By size**	
Size	Number of boxes
Big	
Small	

Sue has a collection of stickers. Help her sort her stickers in two ways. Use tally marks ‖‖ to record the data.

②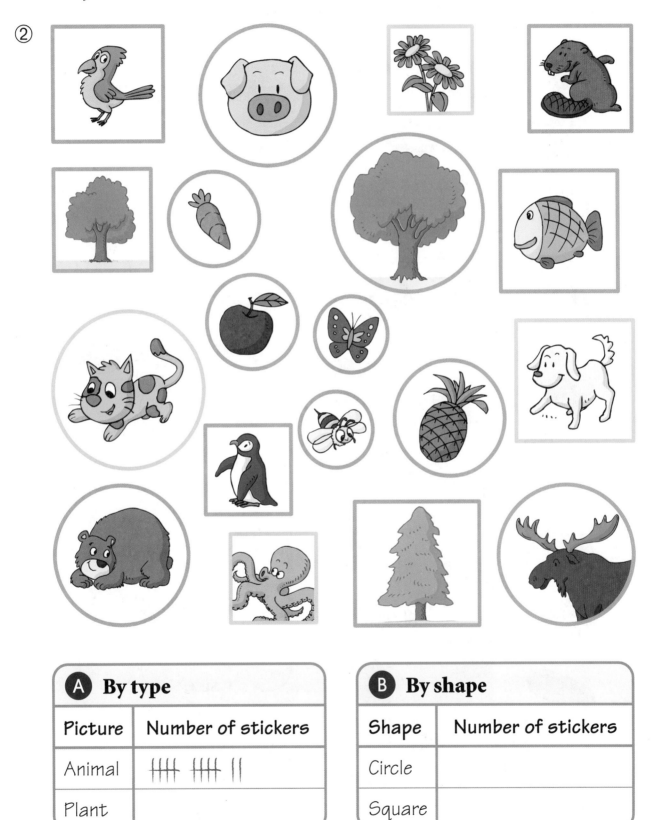

Ⓐ **By type**	
Picture	Number of stickers
Animal	‖‖ ‖‖ ‖
Plant	

Ⓑ **By shape**	
Shape	Number of stickers
Circle	
Square	

The children drew their favourite fast food on the board. Show their preferences. Colour a circle for each food item that you see and cross out ✗ each picture that you have counted.

③

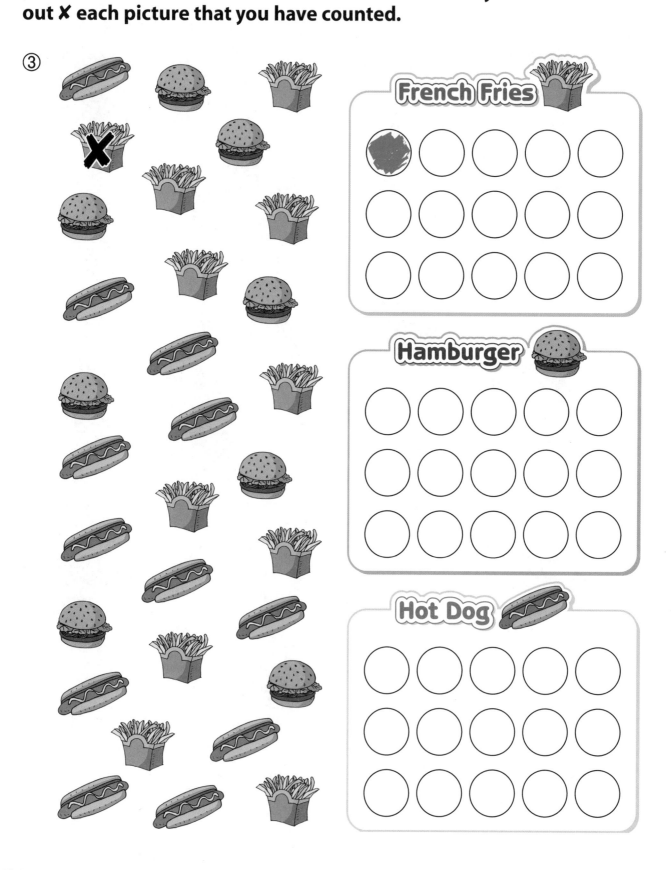

Help Jenny sort her things into 3 groups. Write the rules. Colour a circle for each item you see and cross out X each picture that you have counted.

④

Look at the cards above. Answer Jenny's question.

⑤

Which thing do I have the most of?

_____

Pictographs

- Read pictographs and use comparative words to describe the data.
- Make pictographs to display data.

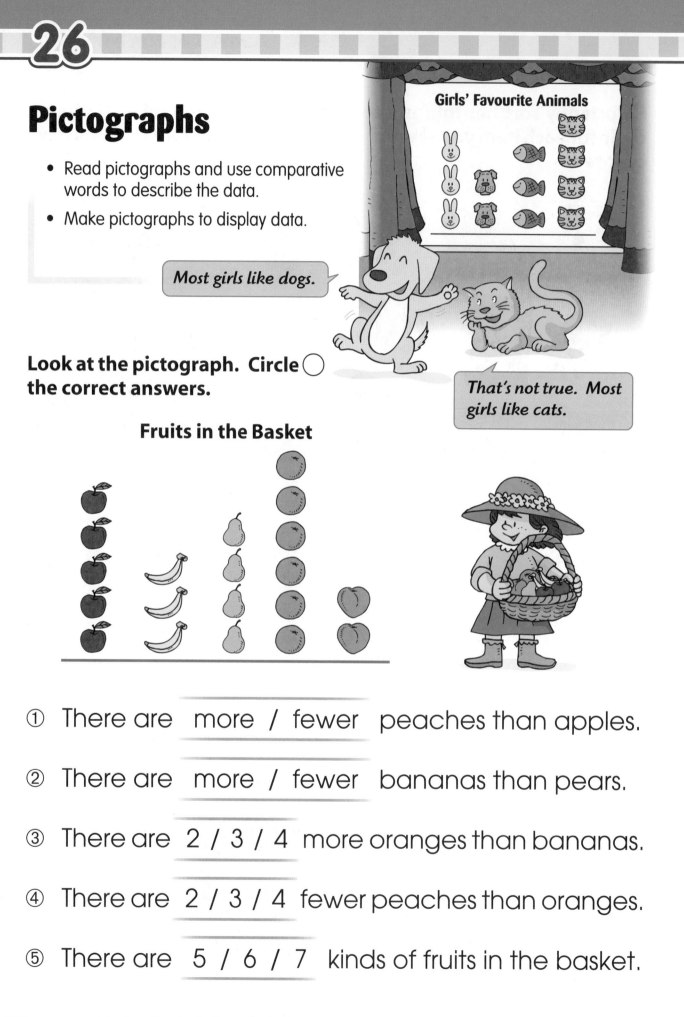

Girls' Favourite Animals

Most girls like dogs.

That's not true. Most girls like cats.

Look at the pictograph. Circle ◯ the correct answers.

Fruits in the Basket

① There are   more / fewer   peaches than apples.

② There are   more / fewer   bananas than pears.

③ There are 2 / 3 / 4 more oranges than bananas.

④ There are 2 / 3 / 4 fewer peaches than oranges.

⑤ There are 5 / 6 / 7 kinds of fruits in the basket.

Look at the pictograph.   Answer the questions.

Favourite Sports in Mrs. Smith's Class

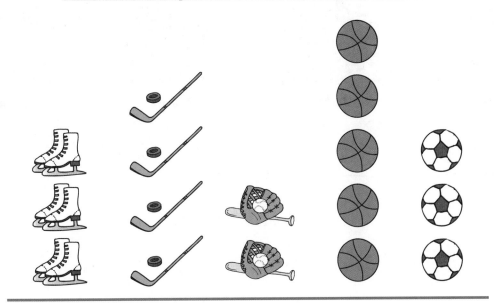

⑥ How many children like hockey?   _____ children

⑦ How many children like soccer?   _____ children

⑧ How many more children like hockey than baseball?   _____ more

⑨ Which sport do most children like?   _____

⑩ If 2 girls like basketball, how many boys like basketball?   _____ boys

⑪   *I'm in Mrs. Smith's class. I don't like ball games. Do you know which sport is my favourite?*

_____

See how many stickers the children have. Help them colour the pictograph to show the information. Then answer the questions.

⑫ **Children's Stickers**

⑬ Who has the most stickers? _____

⑭ Who has the fewest stickers? _____

⑮ How many more stickers does
Susan have than George? _____ more

See how many fish the cats have. Help them colour the pictograph to show the information. Then answer the questions.

⑯ **Number of Fish Each Cat Has**

Sue 5 fish

Leon 6 fish

Lily 4 fish

Ted 6 fish

Sam 7 fish

Sue   Leon   Lily   Ted   Sam

⑰ Who has the most fish? _____

⑱ Who has the fewest fish? _____

⑲ How many fish do Leon and Ted have? _____ fish

⑳ How many fish do the cats have in all? _____ fish

㉑ *If I take away 9 fish from the cats, how many fish will they have left?*

_____ fish

Concrete Graphs

- Read and describe data presented in concrete graphs.
- Complete concrete graphs to show data.

Food on the Table

Yummy!

There are 2 hamburgers, 4 hot dogs, 5 chicken nuggets, and 3 pieces of cheese.

Look at the graph. Fill in the blanks.

Animals on Mr. Smith's Farm

① There are _____ cows, _____ pigs, _____ hens, and _____ ducks.

② There are _____ kinds of animals on Mr. Smith's Farm.

③ There are _____ more chickens than cows.

④ If 5 piglets are born, there will be _____ pigs in all.

⑤ If each hen lays 3 eggs, _____ eggs are laid in all.

See how the children in Mrs. Green's class go to school. Use the graph to answer the questions.

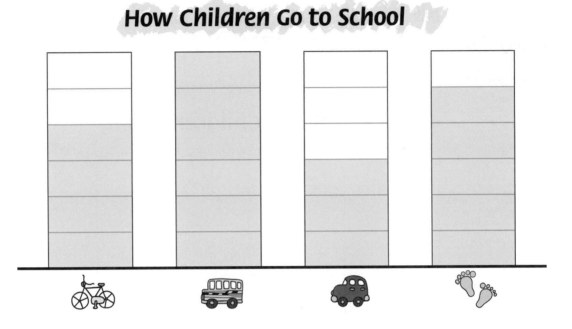

How Children Go to School

⑥ How many children go to school

     a.   by bike?   ____ children

     b.   on foot?   ____ children

⑦ How many more children go to school by school bus than by car?   ____ more

⑧ If 2 girls go to school on foot, how many boys go to school on foot?   ____ boys

⑨ By which way do most children go to school?   _____

⑩

> *I need to wear a helmet when I go to school. How do I go to school?*

_____

See what drinks the children in Mrs. Taylor's class want to have. Colour to complete the graph and answer the questions.

Drink	Milk	Juice	Hot Chocolate	Pop	Slush	Water
No. of Children	|||||	|||||			|||	||||| ||	||||

⑪

Drinks that the Children Want

⑫ How many children like

    a.   juice? _____ children

    b.   water? _____ children

⑬ How many children are there in Mrs. Taylor's class? _____ children

⑭

> In which season do you think I did this survey, summer or winter? Why?

_____

See how many combos Uncle Bill wants to order for the party. Help him colour the concrete graph to show his order. Then answer the questions.

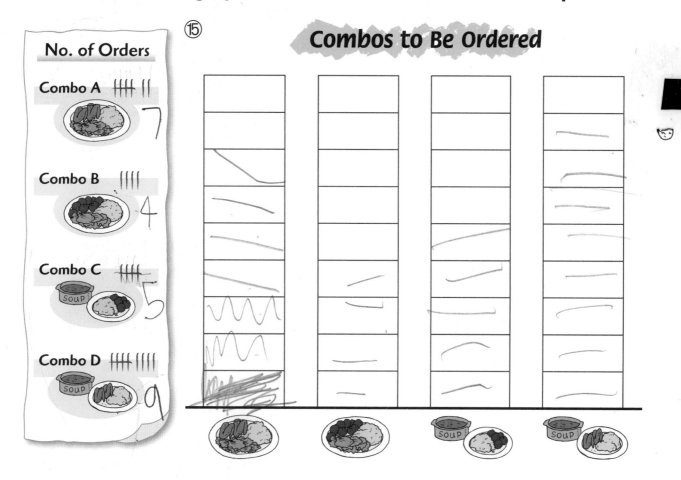

⑮

Combos to Be Ordered

No. of Orders

Combo A |||| || 7

Combo B |||| 4

Combo C |||| | 5

Combo D |||| |||| 9

⑯ How many more Combo Ds will Uncle Bill order than Combo Bs? _____5_ more

⑰ Which combo will he order the most? D

⑱ How many combos will be ordered in all? _____ combos

⑲ *If I take all the combos with chicken wings, how many combos do I have?*

_____

Probability

- Use words such as "impossible", "unlikely", "less likely", "more likely", and "certain" to describe the likelihood of something happening.

Impossible!

I'll be bigger than you one day.

Which of the following are likely to occur? Colour them.

①

②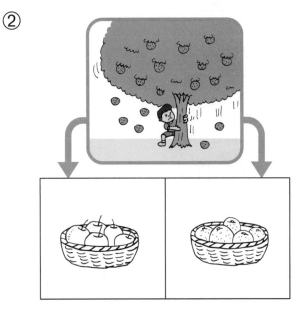

③

④

Write "impossible" or "certain" to describe each pair of pictures.

⑤

a. _____

b. _____

⑥

a. _____

b. _____

⑦

a. _____

b. _____

⑧

a. _____

b. _____

Read what the children say. Then write "impossible", "unlikely", "likely", and "certain" to describe the chances.

⑨ *I've just had a big dinner, but I'll be hungry after one minute.*

_____

⑩ *My brother has a bad cold and Mom has just taken him to the doctor's. My brother will feel better soon afterwards.*

_____

⑪ *I'll finish two bottles of water on my outing tomorrow.*

_____

⑫ It is _____ that I will have a big plate of seafood for breakfast.

⑬ It is _____ that I will have two sausages and one egg for breakfast.

⑭ It is _____ that I will finish eating breakfast in an hour.

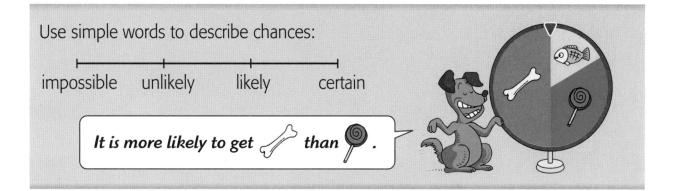

Use simple words to describe chances:

| impossible | unlikely | likely | certain |

It is more likely to get 🦴 than 🍭.

Look at the pictures. Fill in the blanks with "more" or "less".

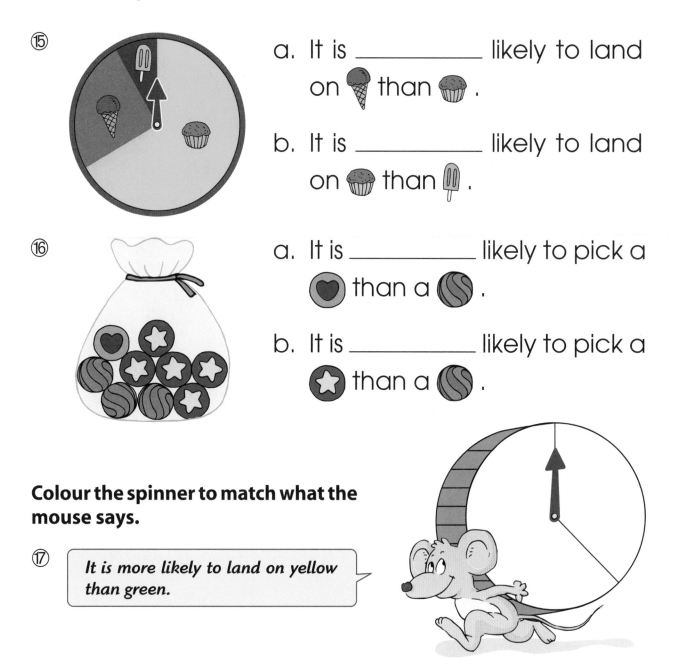

⑮

a. It is _____ likely to land on 🍦 than 🧁.

b. It is _____ likely to land on 🧁 than 🍦.

⑯

a. It is _____ likely to pick a ❤️ than a 🌀.

b. It is _____ likely to pick a ⭐ than a 🌀.

Colour the spinner to match what the mouse says.

⑰

It is more likely to land on yellow than green.

ENGLISH

A Visit to a
Petting Farm

Today my class visited a petting farm in the countryside. We saw many animals at the farm. There were goats and pigs. They were fun to watch.

We also watched the farmer milk his cow. He let us try, but it was not easy.

There were some ponies too. We all had a chance to ride. My pony's name was Blaze. It was a lot of fun.

There was a strawberry patch at the petting farm. We all picked some strawberries and ate them after lunch. They tasted so sweet!

I had a great day at the petting farm.

A. **Complete the sentences with the correct words.**

~~milk~~   patch   ~~countryside~~   sweet   ~~animals~~   ~~ponies~~

1. The petting farm is in the _Countryside_ .

2. The _animals_ on the farm were fun to watch.

3. The farmer let us _milk_ the cow.

4. We also rode on _ponies_ .

5. We picked strawberries on a _patch_ .

6. The strawberries were _sweet_ .

B. **Circle ◯ the words in (A) in the word search.**

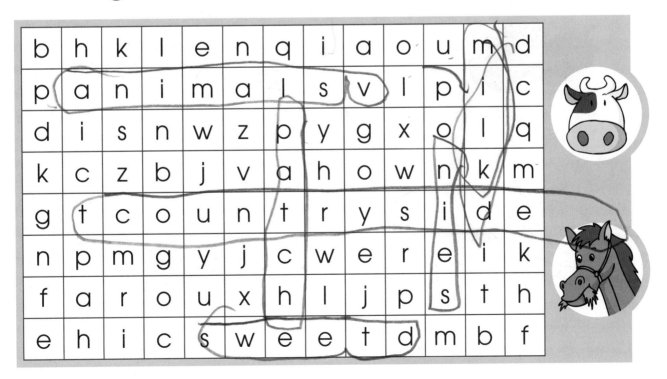

b	h	k	l	e	n	q	i	a	o	u	m	d
p	a	n	i	m	a	l	s	v	l	p	i	c
d	i	s	n	w	z	p	y	g	x	o	l	q
k	c	z	b	j	v	a	h	o	w	n	k	m
g	t	c	o	u	n	t	r	y	s	i	d	e
n	p	m	g	y	j	c	w	e	r	e	i	k
f	a	r	o	u	x	h	l	j	p	s	t	h
e	h	i	c	s	w	e	e	t	d	m	b	f

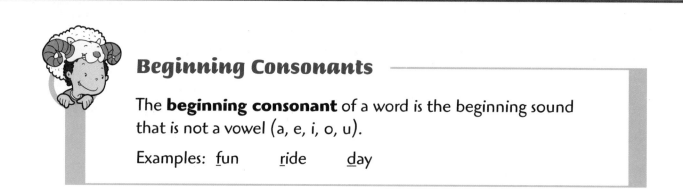

Beginning Consonants

The **beginning consonant** of a word is the beginning sound that is not a vowel (a, e, i, o, u).

Examples: <u>f</u>un   <u>r</u>ide   <u>d</u>ay

C. **Say the thing in each picture. Colour the correct beginning consonant.**

1.

p
b

2.

s
f

3.

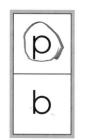

z
s

4.

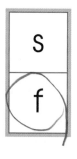

m
b

5.

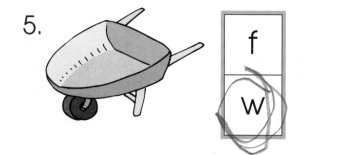

f
w

6.

h
k

D. **Look at the pictures. Help the boy fill in the beginning consonants of the farm animals.**

You are a...

1. g Goat

2. Duck

3. Bunny

4. Cow

5. Turkey

6. Pony

7. Rooster

8. Pig

It is fun to travel on water. Read about the different kinds of boats below.

Canoe – This is a small, long boat. It was first made by the First Nations peoples. It was made of animal skin or tree bark. Now, it is made of fibreglass.

Kayak – This small boat was first made by Canada's northern Aboriginal people. They made it from sealskin. Kayaking is a popular sport now.

Sailboat – A sailboat has large sails and a tall mast. It moves when the wind blows.

Ocean liner – This is a large ship that carries people across the oceans and seas. These people are on holiday. There are swimming pools, shops, restaurants, and even movie theatres on ocean liners.

Over the Ocean Blue

A. Unscramble the letters and write the names of the boats.

otisalba

1. SAILBOAT

cnoae nlire

2. OCEAN LINER

akkay

3. KAYAK

eacon

4. CANOE

B. Check ✔ the things you can find on an ocean liner.

1. Wonder Gifts ✔

2. SCHOOL ✗

3. Special ✔

4. ✗

5. ✗

6. ✔

AEIOU Y

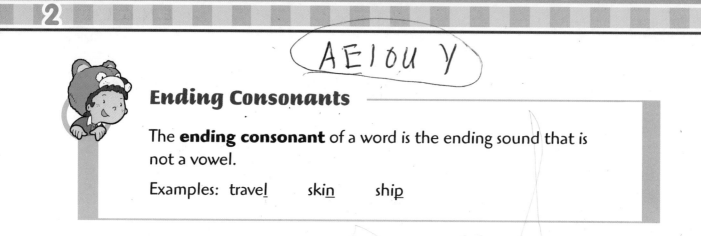

Ending Consonants

The **ending consonant** of a word is the ending sound that is not a vowel.

Examples: trave<u>l</u>   ski<u>n</u>   shi<u>p</u>

C. **Colour the pictures in each group that end with the sound of the letter.**

1.

2.

3.

D. **Draw a line from each letter to the picture that ends with the sound of that letter.**

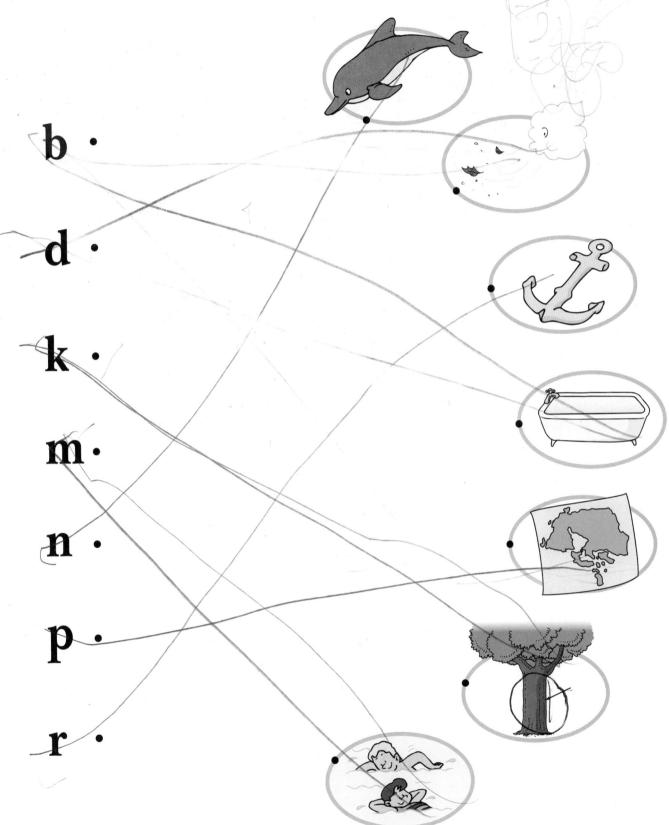

b ·

d ·

k ·

m ·

n ·

p ·

r ·

The Story of the
Greedy Dog

One day a big, brown dog found a nice stick in the park. A little dog saw the big dog's new toy and wanted to play with him. But the big dog did not want to share. He picked up his new toy and ran away. The little dog was sad, but soon he found another friend to play with.

dog so
big a
the
and

On his way home, the big dog walked next to a pond. He looked in the pond and saw another dog! That dog also had a big stick. The big dog decided he would take the stick from the other dog. When he opened his mouth wide, the stick dropped into the pond!

So the big, brown dog had no stick – and no friends – to play with.

take

A. **Find words from the story that mean the opposite of these words.**

1. happy — SAD

2. narrow — WIDE

3. old — NEW

4. closed — OPENED

5. small — BIG

6. give — TAKE

B. **Circle ◯ "Yes" if the sentences are true. Circle ◯ "No" if they are not true.**

1. The big, brown dog found a steak in the park.

   Yes / No

2. The big dog did not want to play with the small dog.

   Yes / No

3. The little dog played with another friend.

   Yes / No

4. The big dog saw another dog swimming in the pond.

   Yes / No

5. The big dog dropped his stick into the pond.

   Yes / No

Short Vowels

Some words with the letters a, e, i, o, or u have the **short vowel sounds**.

Examples: s<u>a</u>d   b<u>i</u>g   p<u>o</u>nd

C. Say the things in the picture. Fill in the missing short vowels.

D. Put a line through the words that have short vowel sounds. Write them on the lines.

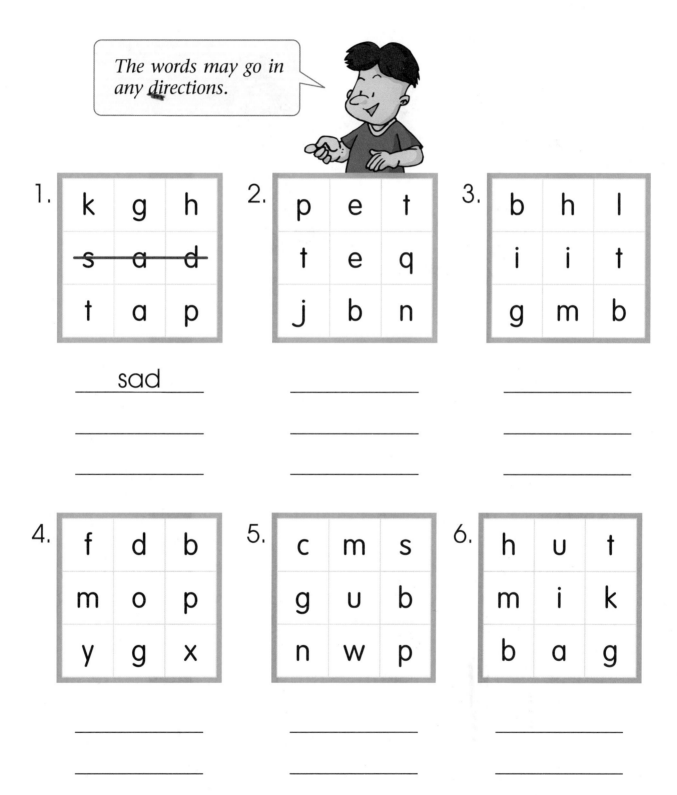

The words may go in any directions.

1.

k	g	h
~~s~~	~~a~~	~~d~~
t	a	p

_____sad_____

_____

_____

2.

p	e	t
t	e	q
j	b	n

_____

_____

_____

3.

b	h	l
i	i	t
g	m	b

_____

_____

_____

4.

f	d	b
m	o	p
y	g	x

_____

_____

_____

5.

c	m	s
g	u	b
n	w	p

_____

_____

_____

6.

h	u	t
m	i	k
b	a	g

_____

_____

_____

Sometimes We Just Like to Look at the Sky...

Sometimes, on a nice day, my friend and I like to lie down on the grass and look up at the big, blue sky. We can see birds and airplanes and clouds.

Some clouds are soft and fluffy. Some are thin and wispy. Some clouds float away in the wind. Some clouds grow big right in front of our eyes.

We think we can see sailing ships and whales. We close our eyes. When we open them, those ships and whales are gone! Then we see some kittens. We watch the kittens run away. This is fun.

A. Colour the ☁ if the sentences are true.

1. The writer likes to look at the sky alone.

2. There are birds and airplanes in the sky.

3. Clouds can be soft and fluffy.

4. Whales swim in the sky.

5. Some clouds look like kittens.

6. It is fun looking at the clouds.

B. What do you see in the sky? Draw a picture to show what you see. Then write a sentence to go with it.

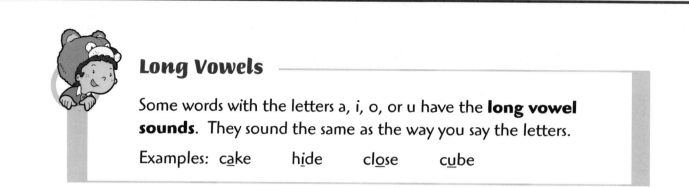

Long Vowels

Some words with the letters a, i, o, or u have the **long vowel sounds**. They sound the same as the way you say the letters.

Examples: c_a_ke   h_i_de   cl_o_se   c_u_be

C. **Complete all the words on each kite with the same long vowel. Say the words.**

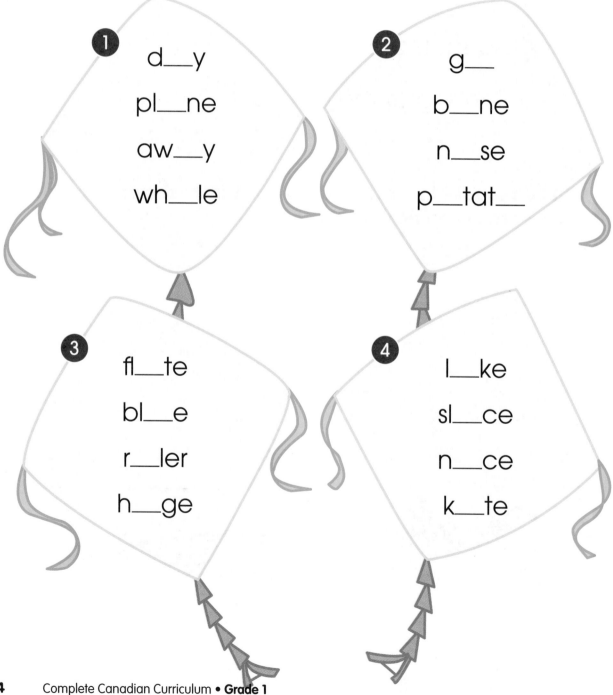

1
d__y
pl__ne
aw__y
wh__le

2
g__
b__ne
n__se
p__tat__

3
fl__te
bl__e
r__ler
h__ge

4
l__ke
sl__ce
n__ce
k__te

D. Say the picture clues. Complete the crossword puzzle.

The letter beside each picture tells you the long vowel that the word has.

Variety
– the Spice of Life

Salty! Spicy! Sour! Sweet!
I love all the food I eat.
Chicken curry! A red beet stew!
Cucumber sushi! Dim sum, too!

I will give all foods a try
From jambalaya to apple pie.
Healthful food from all sorts of places
Makes healthy bodies and smiling faces.

What's for dinner? I can't wait
For a world of variety on my plate.

A. **Put the words in the correct boxes.**

sushi   sour   salty   dim sum

stew   sweet   apple pie   spicy

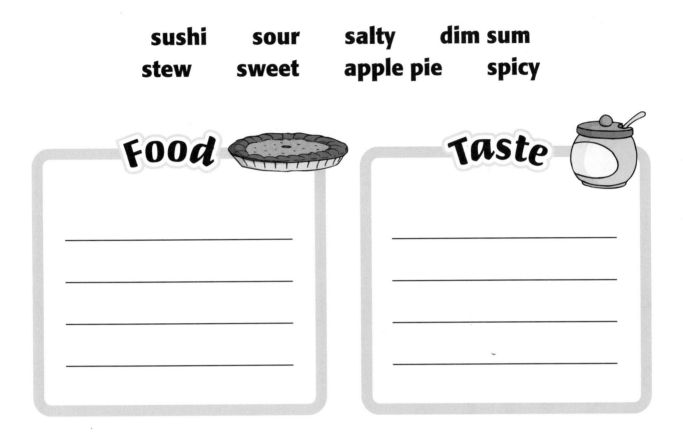

Food

Taste

_____

_____

_____

_____

_____

_____

_____

_____

B. **Complete the table with words from the rhyme.**

1-syllable word	food	
2-syllable word	healthy	
3-syllable word		
4-syllable word	variety	

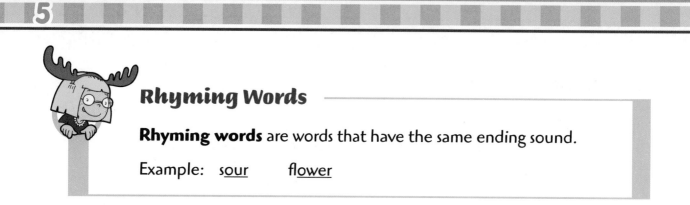

Rhyming Words

Rhyming words are words that have the same ending sound.

Example: s<u>our</u>   fl<u>ower</u>

C.   Draw lines to match the rhyming words.

1.   pie   stew

2.   faces   try

3.   food   spinner

4.   dinner   eat

5.   sweet   places

6.   curry   hurry

7.   wait   mood

8.   too   plate

D. Look at each picture. Say what it is. Colour the word that rhymes with it.

1.

| teacher | thicken | kicking |

2.

| bushy | sea | sit |

3.

| deer | meat | pear |

4.

| handle | smile | cake |

5.

| dice | hike | bye |

6.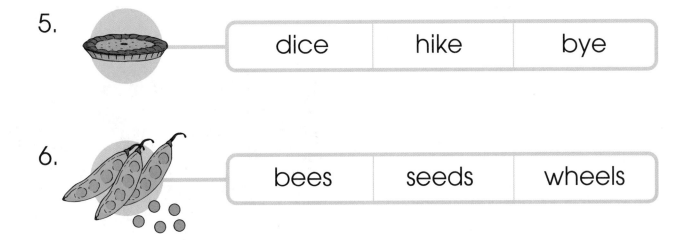

| bees | seeds | wheels |

A Chant from Ghana

Ghana is a country in West Africa. Children there love "do-this" chants. A leader says the line first and everyone else repeats it. As everyone is chanting, they also do the actions.

This is how it sounds:

chay chay koo lay
chay chay koh feen sah
koh fee sah lahn gah
kay tay chee lahn gah
koom ah dayn day
koom ah dayn day
Hey!

This is what the chant means:

Hands on your head.
Hands on your shoulders.
Hands on your waist.
Hands on your knees.
Hands on your ankles.
Hands on your ankles.
Hey!

A.   Put the actions in order. Write 1 to 5.

B.   Write two more lines for the chant. Draw the actions for the lines.

Hands on your _____

_____ .

_____

Nouns

A **noun** is a word that names an animal, a person, a place, or a thing.

Examples: bear   man   country   hand

C. Find the nouns. Colour them with your favourite colour.

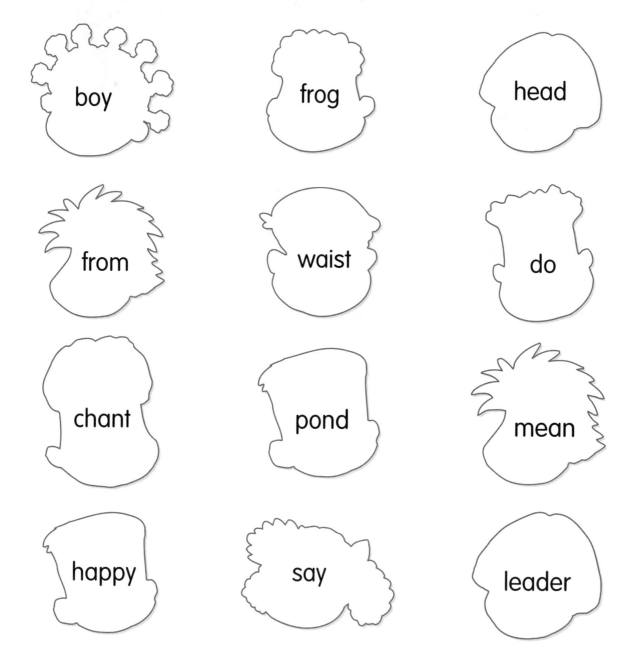

boy

frog

head

from

waist

do

chant

pond

mean

happy

say

leader

D. Circle ◯ the nouns in the sentences.

1. A girl is sitting by the pool.

2. Some fish are swimming in the water.

3. The weather is nice.

4. The sun shines brightly in the sky.

5. The children go to the schoolyard.

E. Draw the pictures. Write what they are.

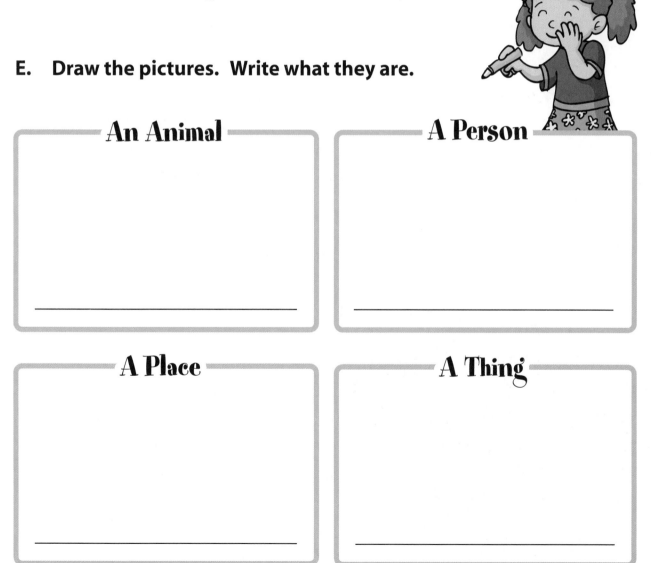

An Animal

_____

A Person

_____

A Place

_____

A Thing

_____

A Letter to a New Friend

Dear Kiyoka,

Hello. My name is Sammy. My cousin Miss Wilson gave me your name and address. She is the English teacher at your school. She asked me to be your pen pal. I am glad to have a friend in Japan!

Sammy is my nickname. It is the short name for Samantha. I am seven years old. I have a brother named Hugh. He is ten. My mom's name is Mandy. My dad's name is Greg. I have a dog. Her name is Choco. She is big and brown and sweet. We live on a farm in the middle of Canada.

Please write to me and tell me all about Japan!

Yours truly,

Sammy

P.S. This is a picture of my friend Emi, Choco, and me. Emi is wearing a cap.

A. Put the names in ABC order.

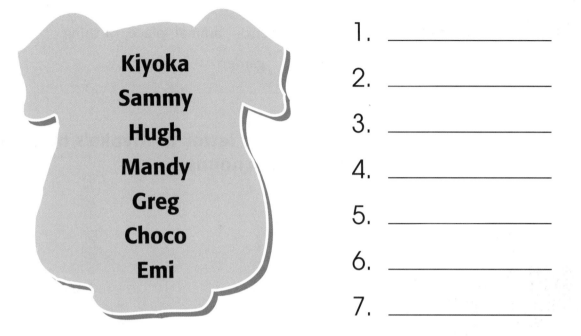

Kiyoka
Sammy
Hugh
Mandy
Greg
Choco
Emi

1. _____

2. _____

3. _____

4. _____

5. _____

6. _____

7. _____

B. Circle ◯ the correct words to complete the sentences.

1. This is a letter from ___ .

    Kiyoka   Sammy   Miss Wilson

2. Miss Wilson lives in ___ .

    England   Japan   Canada

3. Sammy wants to be the ___ of Kiyoka.

    cousin   teacher   pen pal

4. Sammy is the nickname of ___ .

    Greg   Hugh   Samantha

5. Sammy's friend is called ___ .

    Mandy   Choco   Emi

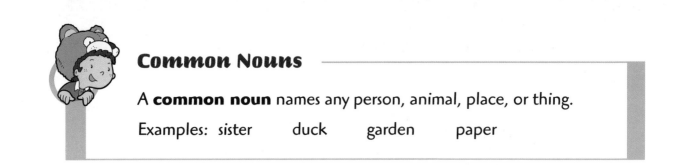

Common Nouns

A **common noun** names any person, animal, place, or thing.

Examples: sister   duck   garden   paper

C. Help Mr. Postman deliver Sammy's letter to Kiyoka's home by colouring the houses with common nouns.

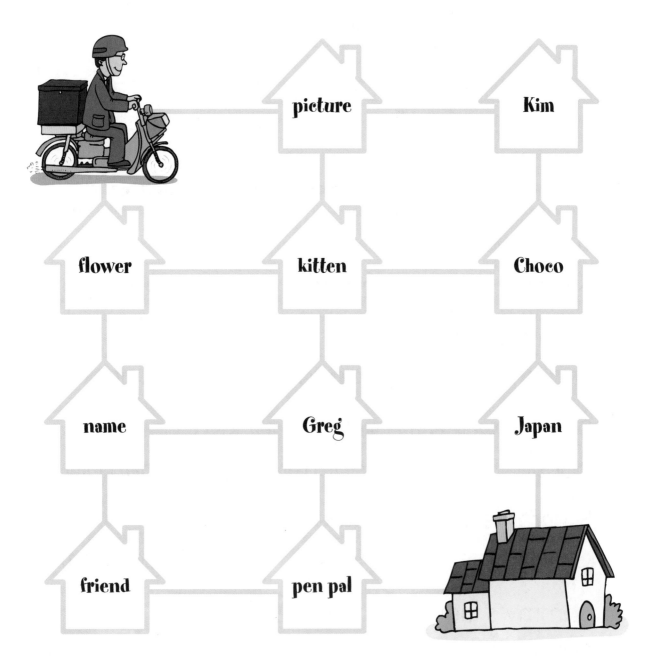

picture   Kim

flower   kitten   Choco

name   Greg   Japan

friend   pen pal

D.   Put the common nouns in the correct  .

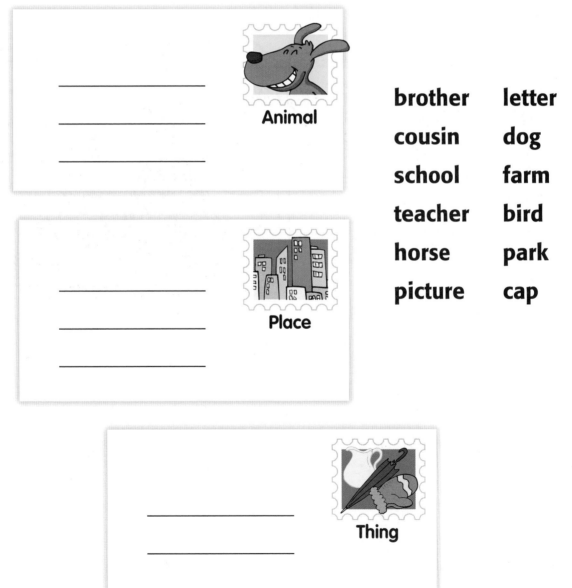

brother	letter
cousin	dog
school	farm
teacher	bird
horse	park
picture	cap

A Letter from Japan

Dear Sammy,

Thank you for your letter. I was very happy to get it from your cousin. Miss Wilson is a good English teacher. She likes to tell us about Canada.

I live in the middle of Japan. It is a very pretty place. People grow rice and fruits here. I am eight years old. I have a sister. Her name is Keiko and she is six. My mother's name is Hana and my father's name is Kenichi. He works in the  city. He goes there by train every day. My grandfather and grandmother live with us.

This is a photo of my sister, our cat Pekko, and me. This is how you write your name in Japanese. Please write back soon!

Your friend,

Kiyoka Nakano

A. Look at the photo of Kiyoka's family. Write the names in the boxes.

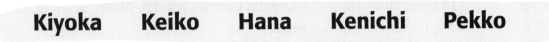

Kiyoka   Keiko   Hana   Kenichi   Pekko

1.

2.

3.

4.

5.

B. Check ✔ if the sentences are true.

1. Miss Wilson is Sammy's English teacher. ____

2. Kiyoka lives in Japan. ____

3. Kiyoka's father works on a train. ____

4. Keiko is Kiyoka's sister. ____

5. There are rice fields near Kiyoka's home. ____

Proper Nouns

A **proper noun** names a specific person, animal, place, or thing. It begins with a capital letter.

Examples: Martha   Nemo   Toronto   Big Mac

C. **Circle ◯ the proper nouns in the sentences.**

1. Sammy lives in Canada.

2. Miss Wilson teaches Kiyoka English.

3. People grow rice in the middle of Japan.

4. Can you write your name in Japanese?

5. The Lion King is an interesting story.

6. It is about a lion named Simba.

7. I go to Lakeside School.

8. Toronto is a big city.

9. The girl has a fat cat.
   She calls it Pekko.

D. **Replace the underlined words with proper nouns. Write the sentences on the lines.**

Don't forget to begin the proper nouns with capital letters.

1. <u>My friend</u> likes playing with me.

   _____

2. I feed <u>my dog</u> every morning.

   _____

3. My cousin works in <u>a small town</u>.

   _____

4. He is reading <u>a storybook</u>.

   _____

5. <u>She</u> is the best teacher in my school.

   _____

6. <u>The capital city</u> is a nice place to visit.

   _____

Our Chores

In our family, everyone helps out around the house.

Every morning, before we go to school, my sister and I make our beds. Then we come downstairs for breakfast. When we finish eating, we carry our dishes to the kitchen sink. Then I fill up our dog Jack's bowls with food and water.

Each evening, after dinner, my sister and I take turns to walk Jack with Mom or Dad.

My sister waters the plants. But I am taller than she is, so I have to water the ones on the shelf.

We like keeping our house clean and tidy.

A.   Put the pictures in order. Write 1 to 6 in the boxes.

B.   Draw a picture to show how you help at home. Write a sentence to go with it.

Singular and Plural Nouns

A **singular noun** names one person, animal, place, or thing.

Examples: student   bird   pond   pen

A **plural noun** names more than one. Many plural nouns are formed by adding "s" to the singular nouns.

Examples: students   birds   ponds   pens

C. Look at the pictures. Circle ◯ the correct words.

1. bed
    beds

2. flower
    flowers

3. school
    schools

4. plant
    plants

5. house
    houses

6. mug
    mugs

7. bowl
    bowls

8. book
    books

9. parent
    parents

D. **Look at the picture. Write the words in the boxes. Add "s" to form the plural where needed.**

apple   ball   boy

cat   cup   mop

plate   sink   towel

1.

2.

3.

4.

5.

6.

7.

8.

9.

Mr. Mom

Did you know the "daddy" emperor penguin has a very important job?

When the female penguin lays an egg, she will give it to the father penguin. The egg rests on the father penguin's flippers, and a fold of furry skin on his belly keeps the egg warm. The father takes care of the egg and the mother goes to the sea to eat!

The mother penguin returns about two months later. Her stomach is full of food that she will give to her baby. After the baby is born, the mother penguin will take care of it. Now it is daddy's turn to go back to the sea to find food. He is hungry!

A. Put the sentences in order. Write 1 to 5 on the eggs.

The mother penguin gives the egg to the father penguin.

The mother penguin lays an egg.

The father penguin goes to find food.

The mother penguin goes to find food in the sea.

The mother penguin returns with food for the baby.

B. What do you think the emperor penguin eats? Draw a picture of an emperor penguin finding food in the sea. Fill in the blank to complete the sentence.

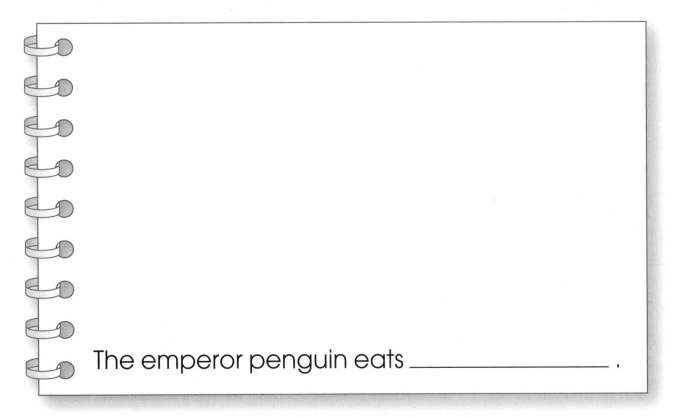

The emperor penguin eats _____ .

Sentences

A **sentence** is a group of words that tells a complete thought about someone or something. It begins with a capital letter and ends with a period (.).

Example: The baby is born.

C. Colour the if the group of words forms a sentence.

1. In this world.

2. The emperor penguins are cute.

3. The father takes care of.

4. and find food.

5. Penguins have flippers.

6. She gives the food to the baby.

7. They are very hungry.

8. Two months later.

9. The father returns.

D. Match the groups of words to form sentences. Write the letters.

1. Kelly likes _____   **A** picture.

2. She is drawing _____   **B** a big egg.

3. A baby penguin _____   **C** drawing.

4. The penguin is _____   **D** cute.

5. I love her _____   **E** is coming out of it.

E. Look at the picture. Write two sentences about it.

1. _____

2. _____

Perogies

Many Canadians love perogies. A perogy is like a dumpling. You fill a pocket of dough with a mixture of mashed potatoes and cheese. You can eat them boiled or fried. They taste great with fried onions and melted butter, and some sour cream.

You can make perogies in other flavours, too. Some people put sour cabbage in their perogies. Others like to put fruit inside, such as bits of plum or peach.

A. Colour the things used for making and eating perogies.

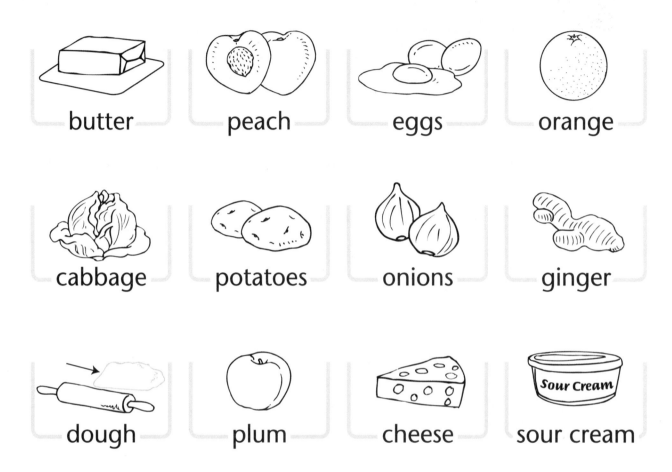

butter   peach   eggs   orange

cabbage   potatoes   onions   ginger

dough   plum   cheese   sour cream

B. Replace the underlined words with words from the passage.

1. <u>A lot of</u> people eat perogies with fried onions. _____

2. They <u>stuff</u> the Christmas stocking with small toys. _____

3. We all <u>enjoy</u> tacos. _____

4. This ice cream is <u>really nice</u>. _____

Telling Sentences

A **telling sentence** tells about someone or something. It begins with a capital letter and ends with a period (.).

Example: You can eat perogies with melted butter.

C. Check ✔ the box if the group of words forms a telling sentence.

1. My grandma makes great perogies. ☐

2. We eat them with sour cream. ☐

3. Can I put strawberries in them? ☐

4. I love them fried. ☐

5. Wow, yummy! ☐

6. Could I have some more? ☐

D. Write the telling sentences correctly.

1. i like perogies

   _____

2. tony loves toast with jam

   _____

3. ice cream is kim's favourite

   _____

4. we all enjoy eating perogies

   _____

E. Draw your favourite food. Write a sentence about it.

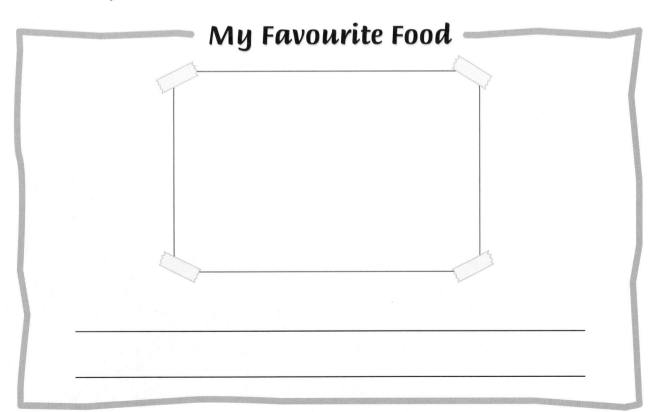

My Favourite Food

   _____

   _____

The Sun and the Wind

One day the sun and the wind were watching a man walk in the park. He was wearing a big, heavy coat.

"I'm so strong," said the wind. "I can blow that coat off the man."

The sun smiled. "Go ahead! Show me," said the sun.

The wind began to blow. It blew and blew. It was so hard for the man to walk in the wind! But the wind could not blow the coat off the man's body.

"Watch me," said the sun.

The sun shone bright and hot. Soon, the man stopped walking. He wiped his forehead with his handkerchief. Then he took off his coat!

A. **Help the wind blow the wrong letters away from the misspelled words. Cross out ✗ the letters and write the correct spellings on the lines.**

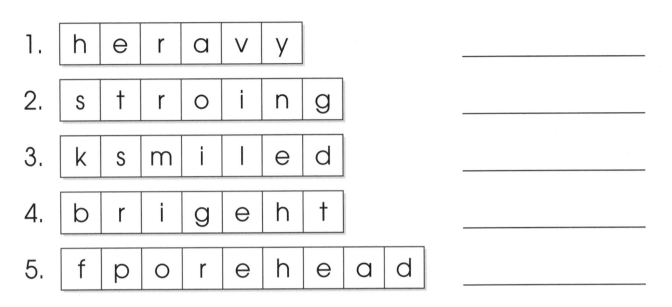

1. | h | e | r | a | v | y | _____

2. | s | t | r | o | i | n | g | _____

3. | k | s | m | i | l | e | d | _____

4. | b | r | i | g | e | h | t | _____

5. | f | p | o | r | e | h | e | a | d | _____

B. **Circle ◯ the correct words to complete the sentences.**

1. The man was in the __ .

   park   school   backyard

2. The man was wearing a __ .

   thin coat   heavy jumper   heavy coat

3. It was __ to walk in the wind.

   easy   hard   fun

4. The man wiped his forehead with his __ .

   coat   hand   handkerchief

Asking Sentences

An **asking sentence** asks about someone or something. It begins with a capital letter and ends with a question mark (?).

Example: What do you like?

C. **Check ✔ "Yes" for asking sentences. Check ✔ "No" for those that are not.**

	Yes	No
1. Let's play a game.	☐	☐
2. Can you make him take off his coat?	☐	☐
3. Is the wind strong?	☐	☐
4. What a hot day!	☐	☐
5. How can you do that?	☐	☐
6. I will surely win next time.	☐	☐
7. Can I join you?	☐	☐

D. Draw lines to match the two parts to form asking sentences.

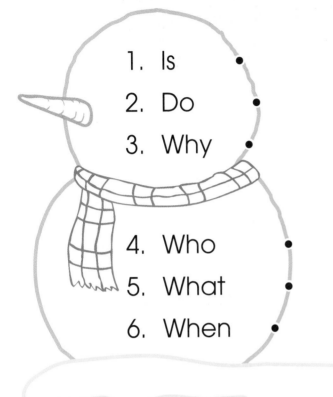

1. Is

2. Do

3. Why

4. Who

5. What

6. When

• can we do in winter?

• is the winter so long?

• will the snow stop?

• likes snowy days?

• it cold in the fall?

• you like fluffy snow?

E. Write the asking sentences correctly.

1. is it windy outside

_____

2. do you have a thicker coat

_____

3. where are you going

_____

4. are you coming with me

_____

Duck Hunting
A Story from China

One day, two duck hunters went out to hunt some ducks. Soon, a big duck came by. Both men wanted to catch the duck. The duck flew closer and closer.

"That duck will be very good in our soup," said the first man. "I love soup."

"No," said the other man. "When I catch this duck, I will roast it. A good roast duck is better than soup."

"I don't think so. I like duck soup the most," said the first man.

"But I love roast duck," said the other hunter.

"Soup!"

"Roast!"

The two hunters started to yell at each other, and the big duck flew away.

A. Check ✔ the correct sentence in each pair.

1. The hunters wanted to hunt some ducks.

    The hunters wanted to save some ducks.

    A

    B

2. The duck loved soup.

    The first hunter loved soup.

    A

    B

3. The other hunter would roast the duck.

    The other hunter would fry the duck.

    A

    B

4. The hunters yelled at each other.

    The hunters yelled at the duck.

    A

    B

5. At last, the duck swam away.

    At last, the duck flew away.

    A

    B

B. Write what you think the duck is saying.

Surprising Sentences

A **surprising sentence** shows strong feelings like fear, anger, and excitement. It begins with a capital letter and ends with an exclamation mark (!).

Example: What an interesting story!

C. Colour the 🦆 for surprising sentences.

1. There is a duck in the sky.

2. Wow, that duck is big!

3. Can you catch it?

4. I will make duck soup with it.

5. Nice soup!

6. Yuck! I hate duck soup!

7. Oh no, it's gone!

8. How lucky the duck is!

D. **You are playing a duck hunting game. What will you say when you miss a duck? Check ✔ the correct box.**

☐ Great!

☐ Too bad!

E. **Write the surprising sentences correctly.**

1. what a narrow escape

_____

2. dear me

_____

3. you won't believe it

_____

4. how bad the hunters are

_____

I Like Winter

In Canada we have four seasons: winter, spring, summer, and fall. Some people don't like winter. They think it is too cold. But I love winter! I wrote a poem about it:

My Favourite Season

Winter spring summer fall
I like winter best of all.
The air is cold,
The sun shines bright.
I love to play
In snow so white.

Did you know that some countries have only two seasons: a wet season and a dry season?

A. Look at the pictures. Write the four seasons.

1. _____

2. _____

3. _____

4. _____

B. Complete the poem in your own words.

My Favourite Season

Winter spring summer fall

I like _____ best of all.

_____

_____

I love to _____

_____

Using Capital Letters (1)

Always begin a sentence with a **capital letter**. Use capital letters for proper nouns and the pronoun "I".

Example: <u>M</u>y sister and <u>I</u> will meet <u>N</u>ancy tomorrow.

C. **Underline the proper nouns in the sentences. Write them correctly on the lines.**

1. There are four seasons in canada.   _____

2. algonquin park looks great in the fall.   _____

3. kathleen is going camping this summer.   _____

4. Will albert join her?   _____

5. Let's go to ottawa in spring.   _____

6. Are we staying at windsor hotel?   _____

7. We'll take our dog, oscar, with us.   _____

D. **Check ✔ the correct sentences. Put a cross ✘ and rewrite the wrong ones.**

> *There are only two correct sentences.*

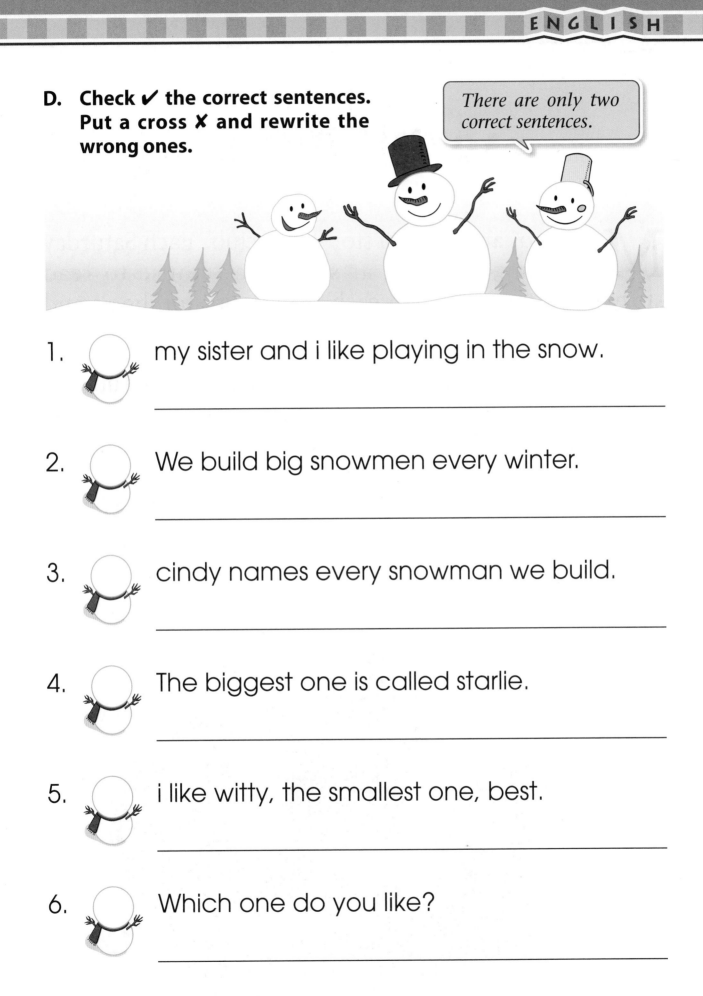

1. my sister and i like playing in the snow.

   _____

2. We build big snowmen every winter.

   _____

3. cindy names every snowman we build.

   _____

4. The biggest one is called starlie.

   _____

5. i like witty, the smallest one, best.

   _____

6. Which one do you like?

   _____

The Storybook Club

My friends and I have a storybook club. Each Saturday morning, we meet at someone's house to read storybooks together. We each bring one storybook and then take turns reading our story to everyone else.

Once a month, one of our parents takes us all to the library. We love going there! Sometimes there is an author at the library, and he or she reads stories to us. Sometimes the librarian reads stories. After storytime, we look at the books on the shelves. My friends and I each choose three books to take home.

I like our storybook club very much.

A. Colour the 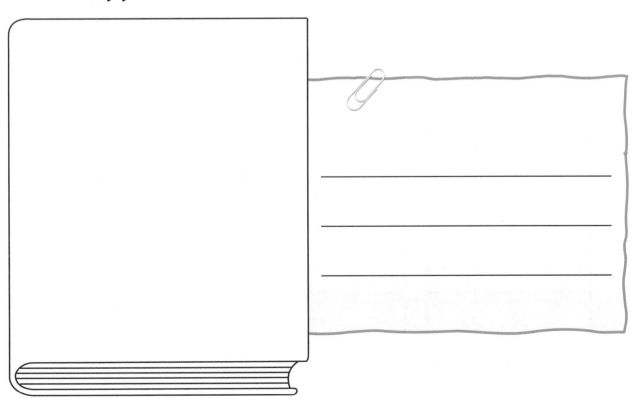 **for the things the children do at the storybook club.**

1. Take turns to read stories.

2. Write a short story.

3. Borrow others' storybooks.

4. Go to the library once a month.

5. Read stories to an author.

6. Borrow some books from the library.

B. Draw a cover for your favourite storybook. Write a sentence to tell why you like it.

Using Capital Letters (2)

Days of the week, months of the year, and festivals all begin with **capital letters**.

Examples: <u>S</u>aturday   <u>A</u>ugust   <u>V</u>alentine's <u>D</u>ay

C. **Write the words correctly in the right places on the calendar.**

Calendar

mother's day   tuesday   easter

halloween   may   november

thanksgiving   july   sunday

wednesday   monday   march

Day of the Week	Month of the Year	Festival

D. Write the sentences correctly.

1. i like christmas.

   _____

2. it is on december 25.

   _____

   _____

3. it is on a thursday this year.

   _____

4. we are holding a party on christmas day.

   _____

   _____

5. i will invite my friend sandra to come.

   _____

   _____

6. i will give her an invitation card this friday.

   _____

   _____

Snow Day

Dear Kiyoka,

There was a big snowstorm last night. When I woke up this morning, there were piles of snow everywhere! My mother turned on the radio, and it said that schools were closed! My mother is a teacher, so she stayed at home with me and Choco.

This is a list of all the things we did today:

Build a snowman.
Play with Choco.
Make chocolate chip cookies (my dad's favourite).
Phone my grandparents.
Write to you!

I like snow days, but I will be happy to go back to school tomorrow.

Your friend,
Sammy

P.S. Do you have snow days in Japan?

A. Check ✔ what Sammy did.

B. What will you do on a snow day? Draw a picture and write a sentence to go with it.

Punctuation (1)

All sentences end with **punctuation marks**.

· A telling sentence ends with a period (.).
· An asking sentence ends with a question mark (?).
· A surprising sentence ends with an exclamation mark (!).

C. Complete the sentences with the correct punctuation marks.

1. How are you, Grandma

2. I made muffins with Mom

3. They are yummy

4. You'll like them

5. Is Grandpa home

6. Where is he

7. Will you come over to our place tomorrow

8. Great

9. I will save some muffins for you

Punctuation (2)

We use a **comma** (,) to separate items in a list.

Example: I love cookies, muffins, and fruit tarts.

D. Add commas in the correct places in the sentences.

1. Jasmine David and I go swimming every Sunday.

2. I love having toast sausages and milk for breakfast.

3. Pink blue green and purple are my favourite colours.

4. You need to bring glue scissors and some clips to class tomorrow.

5. Put your dolls teddy bears and building blocks back in the toy box.

6. My sister likes eating pancakes with jam honey or maple syrup.

7. Spring summer fall and winter are the four seasons in Canada.

8. Do you want lollipops chocolate or cotton candy?

My Mom, the Student

My mom used to work in a hospital every day. She worked in the kitchen. She cooked healthful meals for the people in the hospital.

My mom liked working at the hospital. She liked seeing sick people get better. She started to think that maybe she could help sick people get better too.

My mom made a plan. She was going to go back to school!

Now my mom and I are both students. We study hard. My mom still works in the kitchen at the hospital, but not every day. When she finishes her school, my mom will be a nurse.

I am very proud of my mom.

A. Circle ◯ the correct words to complete the sentences.

1. The writer's mom worked in the kitchen of __ .

    a school   a hospital   someone's home

2. People in the hospital need to eat __ .

    fast food   junk food   healthful food

3. The writer's mom wants to be a __ .

    nurse   doctor   cook

4. The writer is a __ .

    cook   teacher   student

B. Fill in the blanks with words from the passage.

1. Doctors and nurses help _____ people get better.

2. My grandparents eat five _____ a day.

3. My dad saves many people's lives from fires. I am _____ of him.

4. _____ she'll come. I'm not sure.

5. We have to _____ hard to get good grades.

Subjects

The **subject** of a sentence tells whom or what the sentence is about.

Example: The sick <u>people</u> are getting better.

C. Circle ◯ the subject of each sentence.

1. My mom bakes great food.

2. I like her pastries.

3. The chocolate pastries are the best of all.

4. Dad can eat five pastries at a time.

5. Our neighbours sometimes come over to learn baking from my mom.

6. Mrs. Wrights can now make yummy tarts.

7. Her sons like having them for breakfast.

8. They ask their mom to bake tarts every day.

D. Look at the pictures. Complete the sentences with the correct subjects.

children   brothers   girl   boy   dog

1.

The _____ has a cute dog.

2.

The two _____ are playing with their toys.

3.

The _____ is naughty.

4.

The _____ are having fun in the pool.

5.

The _____ is enjoying his ice cream cone.

The Giant Turnip
A *Story from* Russia

One day, a poor farmer wanted to plant his vegetable garden. He liked turnips, but his wife and children did not. His wife liked peas. His son liked beans. His daughter liked carrots. So they picked straws to find a winner. The farmer won.

The farmer planted a turnip seed. Soon, the turnip began to grow. The farmer watered it every day. It grew and grew.

At the end of summer, it was time to pull the turnip out of the soil. The farmer pulled and pulled. But the turnip was so big, it would not come out. His wife came to help him pull. They pulled and pulled. Their son came to help them too, but the turnip would not come out.

Then the little girl came out to help. They all pulled and pulled. The giant turnip came out of the ground. The family took the turnip home. They cooked turnip soup. Everyone loved it.

A. Match the people with the vegetables they liked. Write the letters in the boxes.

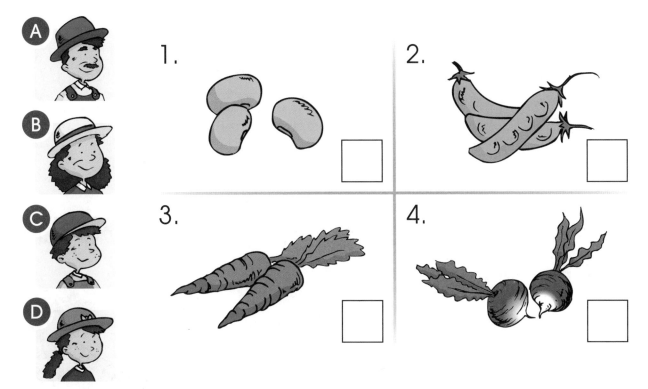

1.

2.

3.

4.

B. Put the sentences in order. Write 1 to 6 on the turnips.

The farmer and his wife tried to pull the turnip out.

Their daughter came out to help too.

The farmer and his family picked straws to decide on what to plant.

They made soup with the turnip.

The farmer planted a turnip seed.

Their son came to help.

Pronouns

A **pronoun** takes the place of a noun. "He", "she", "it", "they", "I", "you", and "we" are pronouns.

Example: The pumpkins are ready for picking. <u>They</u> make great pumpkin pies.

C. Fill in the blanks with "he", "she", "it", or "they".

1. The farmer is in the garden. _____ is taking care of his plants.

2. He likes planting turnips. _____ sometimes grow very big.

3. His wife is cooking soup in the kitchen. _____ smells good.

4. Their daughter loves carrots. _____ drinks carrot juice every day.

5. The farmer's son likes all kinds of beans. _____ wants to have his own garden of beans.

6. Their dog eats everything. _____ likes watermelons best!

D. Circle ◯ the correct pronouns to complete the paragraphs.

1. I He want to grow some 🌸 in the backyard.

2. I He want to give them to 👧 for her birthday next year. 3. He She likes 🌷, so 4. I she am going to grow 🌷🌷 of different colours.

👨 knows a lot about gardening. 5. I He will go to get some 🌷 bulbs with me. 6. He She said to me, " 7. We They will bloom in early spring.

8. We They will take care of the plants together."

Mr. Music's One-Man Band

Hello! My name is Mr. Music and this is my one-man band!

What can you see on my knees? They are cymbals. I knock my knees together and they go CRASH!

What am I holding in my right hand? It is a drumstick. I hit the kettle drum with the stick to make a big BOOM!

What can you see on my ankles? They are bells. I give my legs a shake and the bells jingle and ring.

What can you see next to my left hand? It's a keyboard. With one hand I can play lovely music.

What can you see in front of my mouth? It is a harmonica. It makes a wonderful sound.

Clap your hands, children. Let's sing and dance!

A. Look at the picture clues. Complete the crossword puzzle.

B. Give short answers to the questions.

1. How many members are there in the band?

   _____

2. What does Mr. Music use to hit his kettle drum?

   _____

3. Where are the bells?

   _____

4. What is in front of Mr. Music's mouth?

   _____

Verbs

Most **verbs** are action words. They tell the things you do.

Example: We <u>walk</u> to school every day.

C. Colour the if the underlined word in each sentence is an action word.

1. Dad <u>puts</u> a big star at the top of the Christmas tree.

2. Mom places some <u>presents</u> underneath it.

3. We <u>tie</u> some bells to the tree.

4. They jingle when we <u>touch</u> them.

5. My <u>sister</u> plays the keyboard.

6. I hit the <u>drum</u> with drumsticks.

7. We <u>sing</u> Christmas carols together.

8. Our dog <u>dances</u> to the music.

9. We <u>enjoy</u> a great Christmas.

D. Look at the picture. Write the action words in the correct boxes.

claps   shakes   gives   plays   holds   strikes

1.

2.

3.

4.

5.

6.

My New Dog

"Look at my new pet, Timmy!"

"It is a beautiful dog. Is it an Irish Setter?"

"Yes, you're right! We named him Blaze because he is red like fire."

"Did you get him at a pet shop, Emily?"

"No. My father took me to the dog pound. There were many dogs there. They did not have owners. Some of them looked sad. I chose Blaze. I am happy to have my new dog."

"It is important to care for animals."

"Yes. Having a dog is a lot of work. My parents help me feed him and exercise him every day. Blaze is my best friend."

A. Read the questions. Circle ◯ the answers in the word search.

- Who took Emily to get a new pet?
- Where did they get it?
- What is its name?
- What colour is it?
- What is an Irish Setter?
- How does Emily feel to have a new pet?
- How often does Emily exercise her pet?

	d	B	g			
e	a	n	l	o		c
B	v	q	h	a	p	p	y	k
k	g	e	d	e	z	v	i	m	d	b
s	a	r	s	r	e	d	u	r	o	h
i	t	y	l	j	h	r	p	i	g	e
v	c		w	B	l	g	m		r	j
m	y	d	o	g		p	o	u	n	d
d	o	a	t	x	f	a	t	h	e	r
f	m	y	p	l	i	q	b	s	d	n

Am, Is, and Are (1)

"**Am**", "**is**", and "**are**" tell what someone or something is.

"Am" is used with "I".
"Is" is used to tell about one person, animal, place, or thing.
"Are" is used to tell about more than one person, animal, place, or thing.

Examples: I <u>am</u> a student.
Ginny <u>is</u> my neighbour.
We <u>are</u> good friends.

B.   Circle ◯ the correct words to complete the sentences.

1.   My dog Snow White   am / is / are   a Pekingese.

2.   She   am / is / are   white and fluffy.

3.   I   am / is / are   happy to have her as my pet.

4.   My sister   am / is / are   afraid
of dogs, but she also thinks that
Snow White   am / is / are   cute.

5.   Beef sausages   am / is / are
Snow White's favourite treats.

Am, Is, and Are (2)

"**Am**", "**is**", and "**are**" can be used with the "ing" form of a verb to tell what someone or something is doing.

Examples: I <u>am watering</u> the plants.

The sun <u>is shining</u>.

The flowers <u>are blooming</u>.

C. Look at the pictures. Fill in the blanks with "am", "is", or "are".

1.

   Meg and Joe _____ exercising their dog.

2.

   The children _____ painting.

3.

   Kenny the Clown _____ giving out balloons.

4.

   I _____ learning ballet.

5.

   Porky the Pig _____ playing hide-and-seek with the boy.

Starry Starry Night

Uncle Sam is an astronomer. He gets to look at the planets and the stars. Uncle Sam gave me a big telescope for my birthday. On a clear night last week, we looked through the telescope together. I saw a very bright spot in the sky. My uncle told me it was the planet Venus!

Uncle Sam showed me groups of stars that look like pictures. He showed me "The Big Dipper". It looks like a big pot with a long handle. He showed me one called "The Broken W". It looks like a "w", but it is a little bit lopsided.

I love looking at the starry night sky. Maybe I will be an astronomer too!

A. Read the clues and find the words from the story.

1. a container for taking up water _____

2. The Earth is one. _____

3. person who studies outer space _____

4. leaning to one side _____

5. It makes things far away appear larger and closer. _____

B. Read the story and answer the questions.

1. What is Uncle Sam?

_____

2. What birthday present did Uncle Sam give the writer?

_____

3. What does "The Big Dipper" look like?

_____

4. Which group of stars looks like a "w"?

_____

Adjectives (1)

An **adjective** is a word that describes a noun (person, animal, place, or thing). It often tells how someone or something looks.

Example: The <u>twinkling</u> stars are <u>amazing</u>.

C. Draw lines to match the adjectives with the correct pictures.

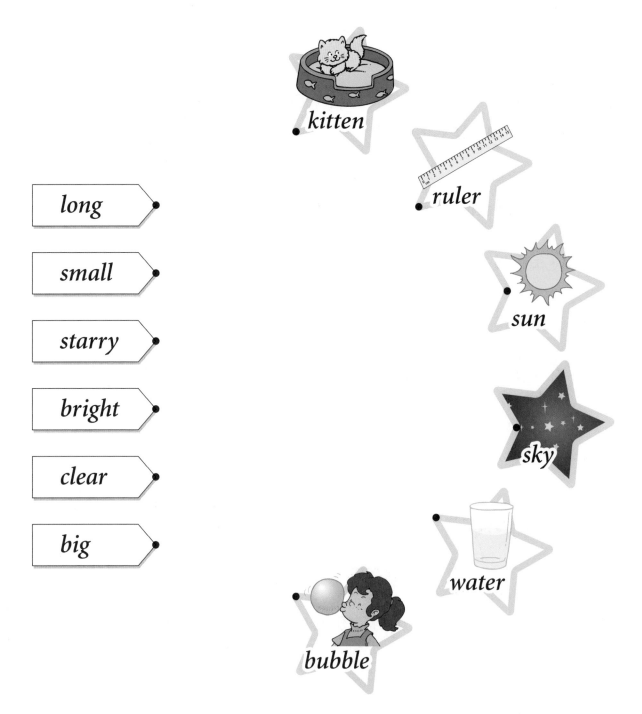

long

small

starry

bright

clear

big

Adjectives (2)

Some **adjectives** tell about the number or colour of people, animals, places, or things.

Example: The <u>three</u> puppies are <u>black</u> and <u>white</u>.

D. Look at the pictures. Fill in the blanks with numbers and colour the pictures.

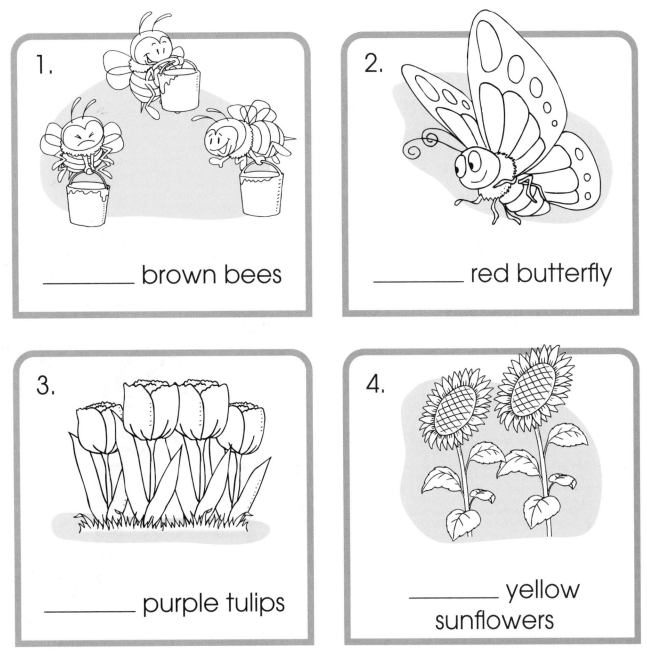

1. _____ brown bees

2. _____ red butterfly

3. _____ purple tulips

4. _____ yellow sunflowers

Hide and Seek

Let's play hide and seek.
Count to ten and I won't peek.
Let's play the game outside
Where you can find a place to hide.

Where can everyone be?
Behind the bushes or up in the tree?
Around the corner or over there?
I can't see anyone anywhere.

But wait. What's that?
I hear a sound.
It's Sam's laughter.
He's been found!

Come out! Come out!
I can see you.
Your dog's wagging his tail
And he gave me the clue.

A. Pair up the words that rhyme. Write them in the trees.

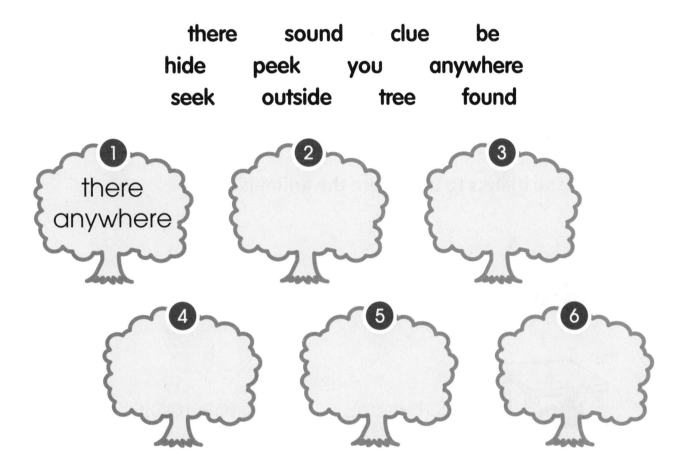

there	sound	clue	be
hide	peek	you	anywhere
seek	outside	tree	found

1. there / anywhere

B. Fill in the blanks with words from the rhyme.

1. _____ inside. Don't let them find us.

2. _____ one, two, and three and the bunny will be gone!

3. It is fun playing this _____ .

4. My sock was lost but now it is _____ .

5. Why is there no _____ for this puzzle?

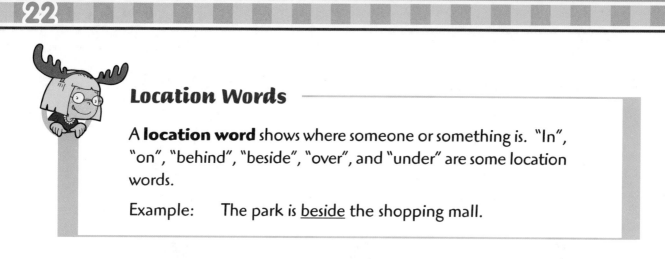

Location Words

A **location word** shows where someone or something is. "In", "on", "behind", "beside", "over", and "under" are some location words.

Example: The park is <u>beside</u> the shopping mall.

C.   Fill in the blanks to tell where the animals are.

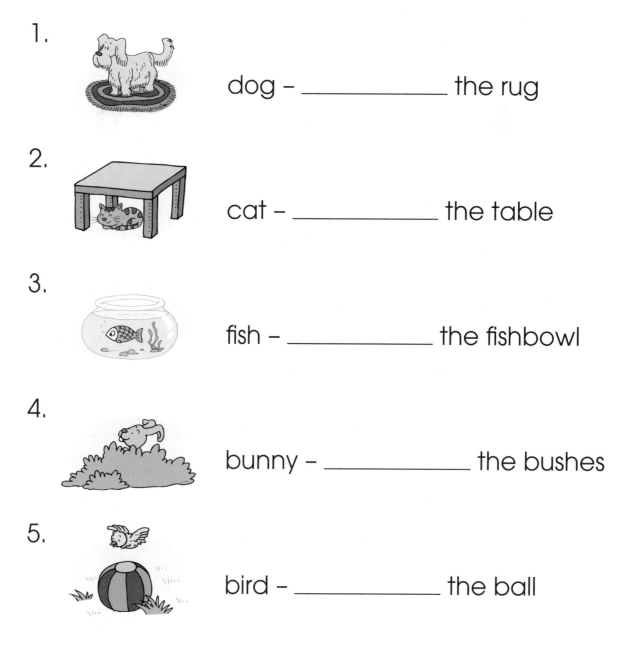

1.   dog – _____ the rug

2.   cat – _____ the table

3.   fish – _____ the fishbowl

4.   bunny – _____ the bushes

5.   bird – _____ the ball

D. Read and complete the picture.

- Draw a sun <u>over</u> the house.
- Draw a fountain <u>beside</u> the house.
- Draw six apples <u>in</u> the tree.
- Draw a bike <u>under</u> the tree.
- Draw a cat walking <u>on</u> the path.
- Draw a girl <u>behind</u> the cat.

My Wobbly Tooth

My bottom tooth came out yesterday. It had been wobbly for a long time. My grandpa told me to wobble it with my finger every day to help it come out.

Every day, my baby tooth got looser and looser. I wanted it to come out, so the Tooth Fairy would visit me.

Yesterday, Grandpa and I had an apple for snack together. When I bit into the apple – guess what – my tooth came out!

I put my tooth under my pillow last night. When I woke up this morning, I found a quarter there!

A.   Read the story.   Circle ◯ the correct word(s) for each sentence.

1.   Every day / Yesterday , my bottom tooth came out.

2.   I wobbled my tooth with my finger / toe .

3.   I wanted Grandpa / the Tooth Fairy to visit me.

4.   I had an apple / apple pie for snack.

5.   I found my tooth / a quarter under my pillow.

B.   Read the clue words.   Complete the crossword puzzle with their opposites from the story.

Across

A. here
B. evening
C. short
D. top
E. on

Down

1. lost
2. alone
3. tighter

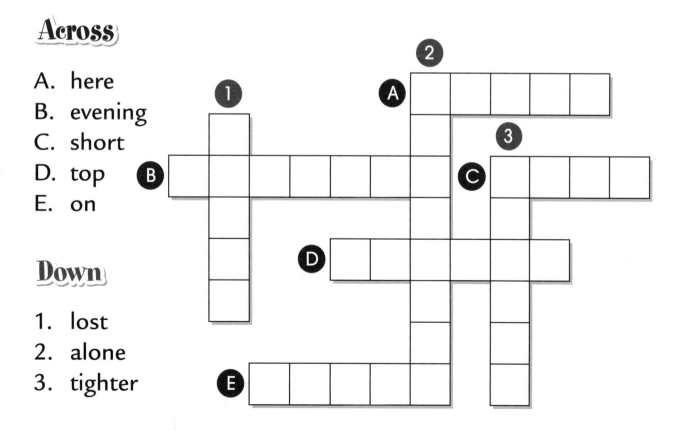

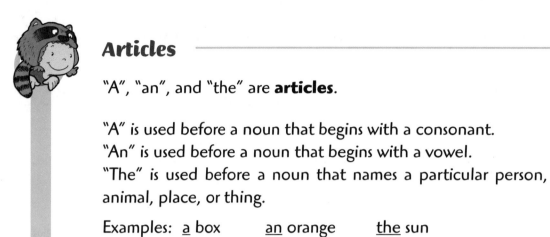

Articles

"A", "an", and "the" are **articles**.

"A" is used before a noun that begins with a consonant.
"An" is used before a noun that begins with a vowel.
"The" is used before a noun that names a particular person, animal, place, or thing.

Examples: <u>a</u> box   <u>an</u> orange   <u>the</u> sun

C.   **Write the nouns in the correct boxes.**

Tooth Fairy

apple

oar

tooth

sky

pillow

onion

string

quarter

world

North Pole

elephant

a
_____
_____
_____
_____

an
_____
_____
_____
_____

the
_____
_____
_____
_____

D. Write what the pictures are with "a", "an", or "the" and the correct words.

owl   dragon   Olympic Games
CN Tower   Easter egg   Earth

1.

_____

2.

_____

3.

_____

4.

_____

5.

_____

6.

_____

My Perfect Day

My perfect day would have a lot of my favourite things in it. The singing birds would wake me up, not my alarm clock. Downstairs, my favourite bowl of porridge would be waiting for me. I would wear my favourite blue dress to school. On my way to school, I would find a "lucky charm", maybe a bright, new loonie on the sidewalk.

At school, I would play with someone new at recess. I would open my lunch bag at lunchtime and find my favourites: a turkey sandwich and a pear! I would go to my friend's house after school to do homework and play.

That would be my perfect day.

A. **Unscramble the letters and write the writer's favourite things.**

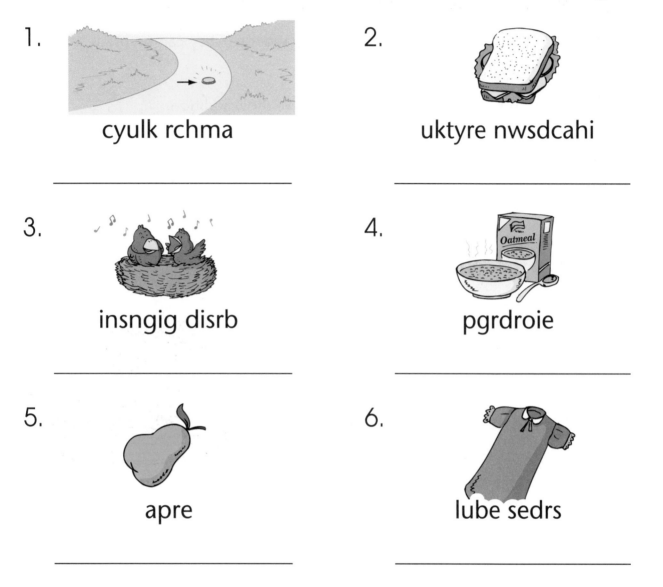

1. cyulk rchma

    _____

2. uktyre nwsdcahi

    _____

3. insngig disrb

    _____

4. pgrdroie

    _____

5. apre

    _____

6. lube sedrs

    _____

B. **Draw your favourite thing. Write a sentence to go with it.**

_____

Connecting Words – And / Or

"**And**" and "**or**" are **connecting words**. They can be used to join words.

"And" is used to join items in a list to show addition.
"Or" is used to join options to show choices.

Examples: Shirley has three toonies <u>and</u> two dimes.

I think either Jen <u>or</u> Dennis will win.

C. Circle ◯ the correct words to complete the sentences.

1. Fries   and / or   pizza are my favourites.

2. Shall we watch a cartoon   and / or   a movie at five?

3. Is this a robin   and / or   a sparrow?

4. I made two new friends today. They are Jessica   and / or   Miranda.

5. I can see some birds   and / or   squirrels outside the window.

6. Which dress do you like, the pink one   and / or   the blue one?

D. Look at the pictures. Complete the sentences with "and" or "or".

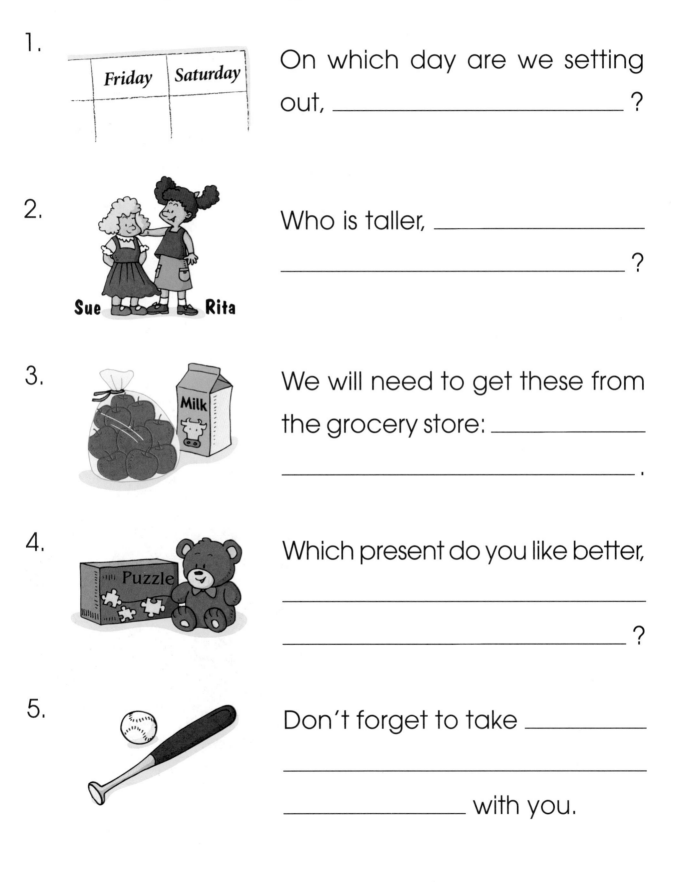

1. On which day are we setting out, _____ ?

2. Who is taller, _____ _____ ?

3. We will need to get these from the grocery store: _____ _____ .

4. Which present do you like better, _____ _____ ?

5. Don't forget to take _____ _____ _____ with you.

Riddles

Riddles are questions that have funny answers. They are like guessing games. Can you answer these questions?

I have a face, but I don't have eyes, or a nose, or a mouth.

I have two hands, but they don't have fingers.

What am I?

Answer: a clock

I have four legs, and you can sit on me.

But...I also have two arms!

What am I?

Answer: an armchair

What starts with "p", ends with "e", and has lots of letters?

Answer: post office

Letters make up words. Letters are also found at a post office.

A. Solve these riddles.

1.

> *I have teeth but I won't bite.*
> *I'm a good friend of your hair.*
> *What am I?*

_____

2.

> *I have no legs but I can run.*
> *You can see me but you can't hold me with your hands.*
> *What am I?*

_____

B. Think of your own riddle. Write it on the lines. Draw a funny picture to go with it.

_____

_____

_____

_____

Connecting Word – But

"**But**" is used to join two contrasting ideas in a sentence.

Example: Chickens have wings <u>but</u> they cannot fly.

C. Check ✔ the correct sentences.

1. Jerry likes chocolate but he likes toffee.

2. The road was slippery but he fell.

3. The weather is nice today but we have to stay at home.

4. The words are small but we can still read them.

5. The song is good but he sings it badly.

6. Nicole wants to join the camp but she is too young.

7. Let's buy an ice cream but share it together.

D. Add "but" with a ∧ in the correct places in the sentences.

1. The movie was long we did not find it boring.

2. This dish does not look nice it tastes good.

3. The girls play volleyball the boys play soccer.

4. The sun is shining it is also raining.

5. I want to eat a Popsicle there are not any left.

E. Join the two parts with "but" to complete the sentences.

- it is friendly
- the sea water is cool
- this one is too sour
- I can reach it

1. Ivan likes juice _____ .

2. The shelf is tall _____ .

3. The dog looks fierce _____ .

4. The sand is hot _____ .

One day, a fox was walking in the jungle. Suddenly, a tiger jumped on the fox. The fox cried out, "I am the King of the Jungle. How dare you try to hurt me!"

The tiger looked at him. He was very surprised. "You are not the King of the Jungle. You are just a fox."

"I am the King," said the fox. "All the animals are afraid of me! Come with me and I'll show you."

The tiger followed the fox. They came upon a herd of deer. When the deer saw the tiger behind the fox, they ran away in fright! Then the fox and the tiger came to some monkeys. The monkeys saw the tiger behind the fox, and they also ran away.

The King of the Jungle

The fox turned to the tiger. "You see how the animals run away when they see me?"

"You are truly the King of the Jungle," said the tiger. He bowed low and let the fox run proudly away.

A. Write the names of the animals.

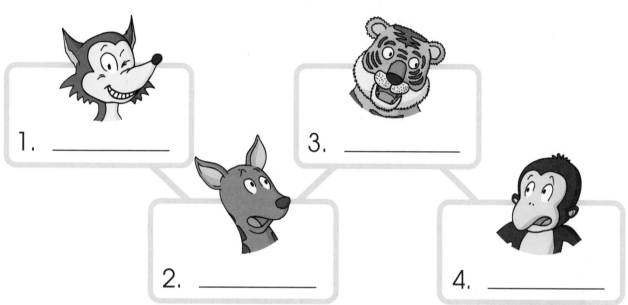

1. _____

2. _____

3. _____

4. _____

B. Put the sentences in order. Write them on the lines.

- The monkeys also ran away.
- The deer were frightened and ran away.
- The fox said that he was the King of the Jungle.
- The tiger tried to catch the fox.
- The fox ran proudly away.
- The tiger bowed to the fox.

1. _____

2. _____

3. _____

4. _____

5. _____

6. _____

26

Word Order in Sentences

The words in a sentence should be put in order to make sense. Changing the order of the words can change the meaning of the sentence.

Example: The dog is walking the girl. (✘)
          The girl is walking the dog. (✔)

C. **Look at each picture. Colour the**  **of the correct sentence.**

1.

The fox was in the jungle.

The jungle was in the fox.

2.

The rabbit chases the fox.

The fox chases the rabbit.

3.

The sun is behind the clouds.

The clouds are behind the sun.

4.

The cat is eating the fish.

The fish is eating the cat.

D. Put the words in order to write the sentences.

Remember to begin each sentence with a capital letter and end it with the correct punctuation mark.

1. like   cheese   mice   eating

_____

2. colourful   flowers   the   are

_____

3. puts   the   she   box   toys   in   the

_____

4. is   a   writing   Benny   letter

_____

5. ice cream   who   strawberry   wants

_____

6. the   hiding   dog   candy   is   the

_____

7. you   are   where   going

_____

My First Visit to the
Dentist

Today I went to see the dentist. It was my first time. I was a little scared, but the dentist was very kind. He told me to sit down on the big chair. We watched a cartoon about a mouse having his teeth checked. It was funny.

Then the dentist showed me some of his tools. Later, I pressed a button, and some water went into the drinking cup.

After that, the dentist told me to lie back and open my mouth. He counted my teeth. Then he checked them carefully. He said my teeth looked nice. He showed me how to brush them correctly. When I was leaving, he gave me a new toothbrush!

I like my dentist. I will go back to see him again in six months.

A. Find words from the story that match the meanings below. Circle ◯ them in the word search.

· good

· large

· the opposite of "front"

· You use it to brush your teeth.

· pushed

· frightened

· the opposite of "close"

· You use it to drink water.

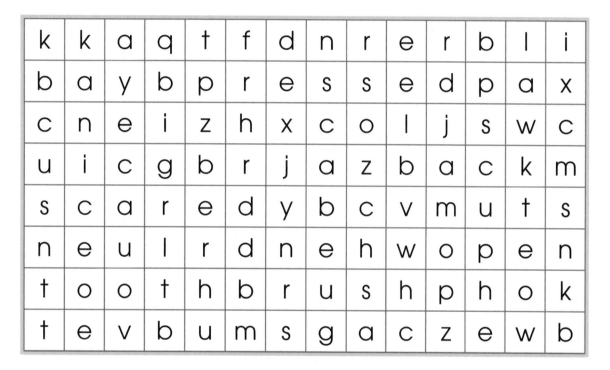

k	k	a	q	t	f	d	n	r	e	r	b	l	i
b	a	y	b	p	r	e	s	s	e	d	p	a	x
c	n	e	i	z	h	x	c	o	l	j	s	w	c
u	i	c	g	b	r	j	a	z	b	a	c	k	m
s	c	a	r	e	d	y	b	c	v	m	u	t	s
n	e	u	l	r	d	n	e	h	w	o	p	e	n
t	o	o	t	h	b	r	u	s	h	p	h	o	k
t	e	v	b	u	m	s	g	a	c	z	e	w	b

B. Give short answers to the questions.

1. How did the writer feel when he went to see the dentist?

_____

2. What was the cartoon about?

_____

3. When will the writer see the dentist again?

_____

Related Sentences

We put sentences that are related together. They should be about the same topic.

Example: The dentist checked my teeth. ~~I want to be a dentist too.~~ Then he showed me how to brush them.

C. **Read each group of sentences. Put a line through the one that is not related to the others.**

1. We are dining out this evening. We will try the new Italian restaurant nearby. The food there is nice. John is hungry.

2. There are many people at the beach. Some of them are swimming and some are sunbathing. It is too cold to go to the beach in winter.

3. Those puppies are cute. We have a new dog. He has a long, brown body. We call him Sausage.

D. **Write the sentences below in the correct places.**

- She will get her eighth teddy bear this summer.

- My aunt has a candy shop.

- He goes fishing every weekend in summer.

1.

_____

_____

It sells candies of different shapes and flavours.

I like the lollipops best.

2.

My dad loves fishing.

_____

_____

I sometimes go with him.

3.

Carrie collects teddy bears.

Her uncle sends her a teddy bear for her birthday every year.

_____

_____

A Day with Grandpa

I like it when Grandpa comes to visit. He always does amazing things with us. Today he said we were going to make a bird feeder!

First, Grandpa took out a pine cone and a bag of birdseed. He told me to get the peanut butter and put some all over the pine cone. Then he told my sister to roll the pine cone in the birdseed.

Next, Grandpa tied a strong string around the pine cone. We went outside and walked to a tree in the backyard. Grandpa tied the pine cone to a branch.

We waited. Soon a bird came and pecked at the pine cone! Grandpa said it was a sparrow. Later, a beautiful blue bird came to get some seed. Grandpa said it was a blue jay. It was exciting! We like watching birds with Grandpa.

A. Look at the picture clues. Complete the crossword puzzle.

Sequencing

Sentences should be put in a logical order so that people can follow the idea.

B. **Match the sentences with the pictures. Write the letters.**

A He then tied the pine cone to a branch.

B I put peanut butter over a pine cone.

C Grandpa tied a string around the pine cone.

D I got the peanut butter from the fridge.

E Soon a bird came and pecked at the pine cone.

F Then my sister rolled the pine cone in birdseed.

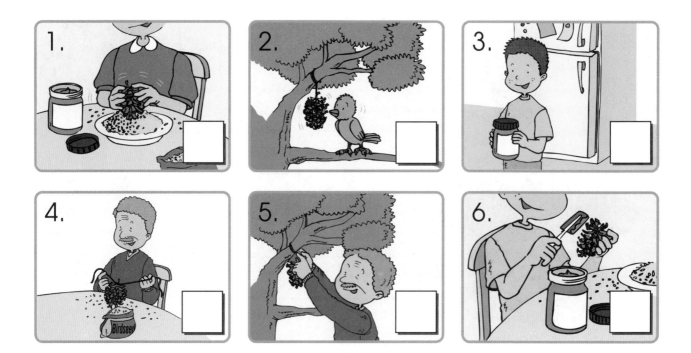

C. Put the sentences in (B) in order. Write them on the lines below.

1. _____

2. _____

3. _____

4. _____

5. _____

6. _____

D. Put the pictures in order by writing the letters in the boxes. Write sentences about them.

☐ _____

☐ _____

☐ _____

SOCIAL STUDIES

What Makes Me "Me"

There is no one like me. I am special for who I am, how I look, and where I live. I am special in many other ways too.

A. Draw yourself on the stage. Then tell everyone about yourself.

My name is

_____ _____.
first   last

I am a

_____.
boy/girl

I am

_____ years old.

B. Write, circle, and colour to tell more about yourself.

Members in my family:

_____

_____

_____

Language(s) I speak:

_____

_____

I am:

friendly

helpful

shy

smart

gentle

funny

creative

kind

_____

_____

My hair colour

My eye colour

I write with my

left hand

right hand

Special People

There are many people around us. They help us in different ways. Each of them has a special job or role.

A. **Write the numbers and the letters in the correct circles to show how these people help you.**

This person...

A helps me with my daily needs.

B brings me letters.

C helps lead my community.

D helps me when I am sick.

E helps me learn at school.

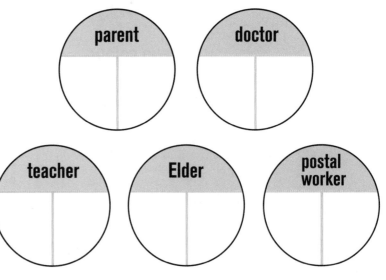

parent

doctor

teacher

Elder

postal worker

B. Draw a picture of a special person in your life. Then write about him or her.

This is

_____ .

name

This person is special to me because _____

_____ .

What I like most about this person is _____

_____ .

Important Places

Some places are important to us. One of these places can be a friend's or a relative's house, a school, a place of worship, or a park.

A. Paste or draw a picture of your important place. Then name the place and fill in the blanks.

My Important Place

- This is the place where I _____ .

- I like to _____ here.

- I usually go to this place on _____ (day of the week).

B. **Look at Sally's map. Read what she says. Then draw a map to show the way from your home to your important place.**

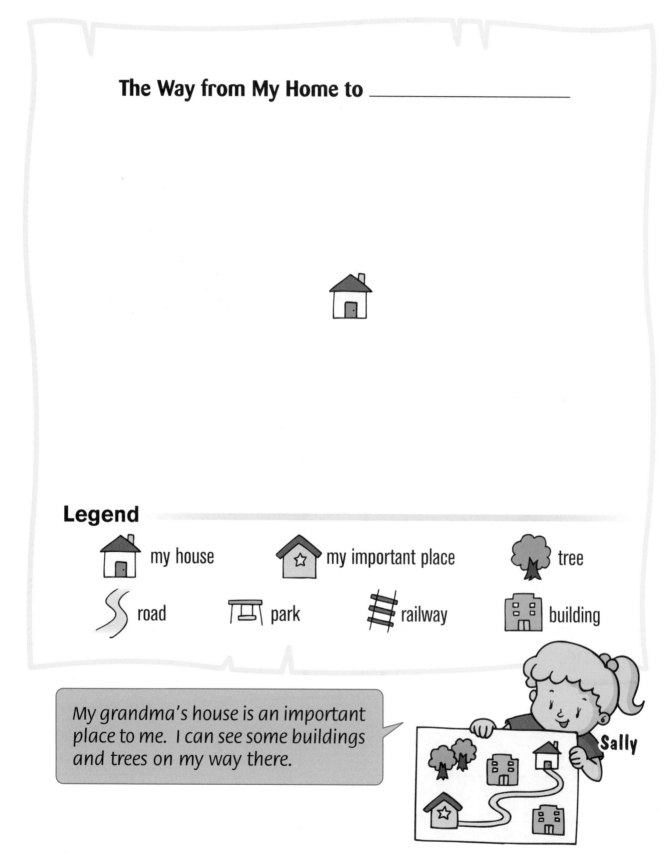

The Way from My Home to _____

Legend

my house   my important place   tree

road   park   railway   building

My grandma's house is an important place to me. I can see some buildings and trees on my way there.

Sally

Special Things

We all have special things. They can be our favourite toys or our pets. These things are important because they are part of who we are.

A. **Talk with two friends who have pets. Have them draw their pets in the boxes and write why their pets are special.**

My dog Teddy is very special to me. Every day after school, I like to play ball with him. Do you have a pet? Why is he/she special to you?

Name:

Name:

So special! _____

So special! _____

_____

_____

B. **Match the pictures with the correct sentences. Then draw and write about your family's special thing.**

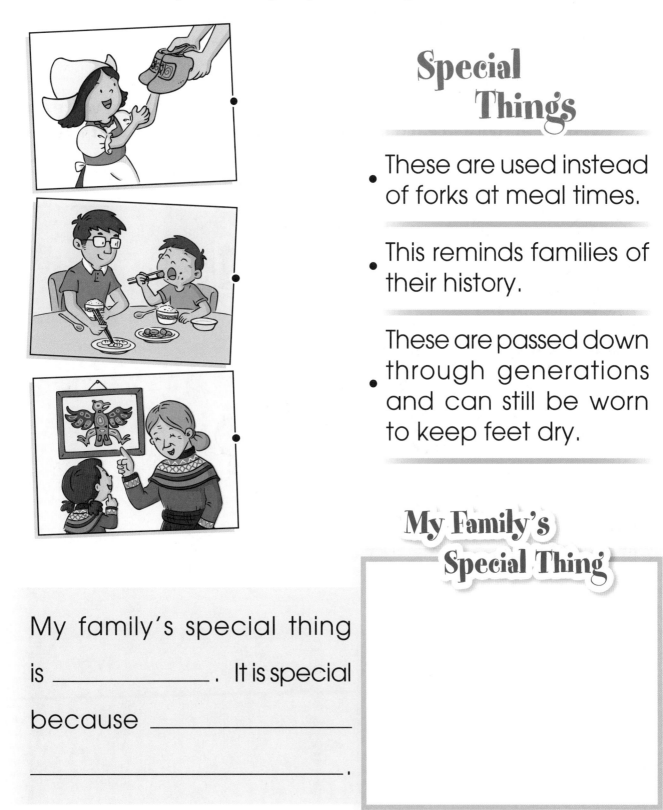

Special Things

• These are used instead of forks at meal times.

• This reminds families of their history.

• These are passed down through generations and can still be worn to keep feet dry.

My Family's Special Thing

My family's special thing is _____ . It is special because _____ _____ .

Special Events

There are many important times in a person's life. A timeline shows a list of important events and when they happened.

A. Write your birth date to start the timeline. Then draw or write an event or activity in each box to show what you did at that age.

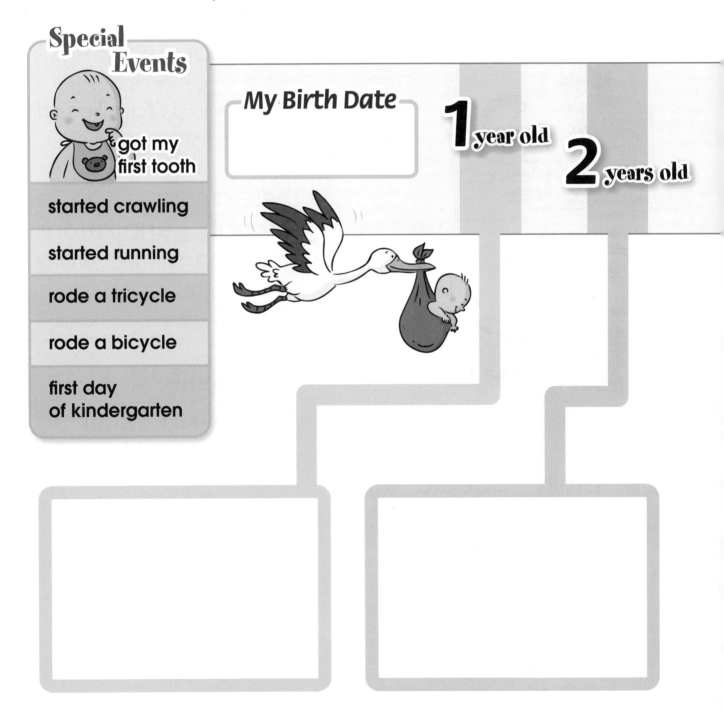

Special Events

got my first tooth

started crawling

started running

rode a tricycle

rode a bicycle

first day of kindergarten

My Birth Date

1 year old

2 years old

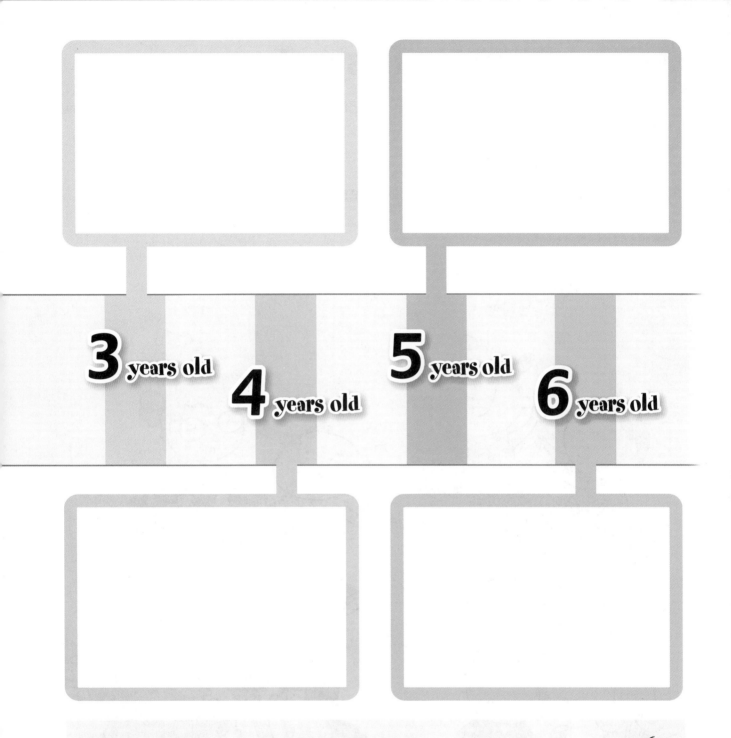

3 years old

4 years old

5 years old

6 years old

Ask your friends about their timelines.

1. Did they learn to ride a bicycle in the same year as you?

2. Did they all enter kindergarten at the same time as you?

Showing Respect

We should respect other people and the world around us. We can show respect in many ways.

A. Check ✔ the people who show respect.

B. Colour the pictures that show people respecting their surroundings. Then draw a line to take Jason to his friend and circle ◯ the correct word.

Jason

O Canada...

We can also show our respect for the environment by **cleaning / dirtying** it.

My Changing Roles

We all have different roles. We have different relationships within our families and our communities that shape our identity.

A. Write the role of each child in the box.

daughter   neighbour   grandson   student

B. **What roles do you have? Draw yourself in the circle. Then circle ◯ your different roles.**

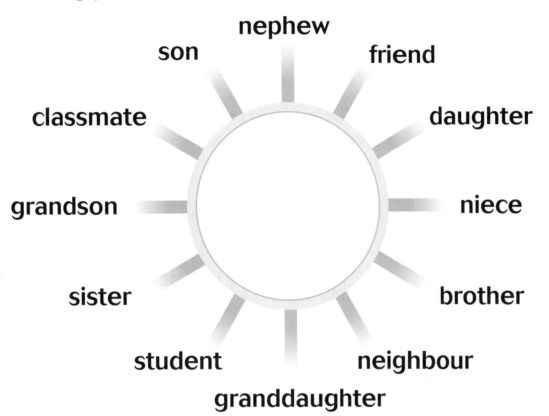

nephew

son   friend

classmate   daughter

grandson   niece

sister   brother

student   neighbour

granddaughter

C. **Draw lines to show the things you would do as a big brother/sister, a friend, or both.**

Things I would do

invite him/her to my •
birthday party

help tie his/her shoes   •

visit his/her house   •

comfort him/her when •
he/she is sad

Roles

• big brother/
sister

• friend

• both

My Changing Responsibilities

As our roles change, our responsibilities change too. Also, we have different responsibilities in different places.

A. Read what Emma says. Circle ◯ the correct roles and check ✔ the new responsibilities she might take up.

At Home

> I was an only child. But now, I have a baby brother.

Her new role:

mother

sister

daughter

Her new responsibilities:

Ⓐ change diapers

Ⓑ sing lullabies

Ⓒ feed the pet

At School

> I have a different role when I am at school.

Her role: cousin   niece   student

Her responsibilities:

Ⓐ finish classwork

Ⓑ drive students home

Ⓒ make friends with new students

B. **As we get older, our responsibilities change. Draw pictures of your changing responsibilities and write about them.**

Idea Bank

make my bed

feed the pet

brush my teeth

do homework

Kindergarten

This is a responsibility I had
when I was in kindergarten.

I _____

_____ .

Grade 1

This is a responsibility I
have now. I _____

_____

_____ .

More Changing Roles and Responsibilities

Our actions and responsibilities depend on our roles and where we are.

A. **Look at the pictures. Write how the children's actions change in different places.**

A At Home:

B At a Park:

Once upon a time...

At School:

In a Library:

Once upon a time...

How the actions change:

A _____

_____

B _____

_____

B. **Parents have different roles depending on where they are too. Read about their different responsibilities and decide whether they are for home or for work. Draw lines to match.**

Responsibilities

- earn money
- read bedtime stories
- buy groceries
- clean up the house
- meet deadlines
- go to work on time

Your parents have lots of responsibilities at home. Do you share any of them? If so, what are they?

_____

_____

Our Interactions with Others

We interact with our family members, friends, and other people around us. Our actions affect others.

A. Read the comics. Describe the people's feelings and actions.

Mom... Mom...

sympathetic   happy   sad

feels _SAd_.

feels _SYMPAtHEtY_.

Don't be scared.

Action!

helps / teases

Thank you!

Action!

ignore   thank

feels _happy_

B. **Look at the pictures. Write how Mickey makes the girl feel in each picture. Then answer the question.**

How Mickey makes the girl feel in

A : BAd

B : UPSET

C : tHANKful

thankful
embarrassed
sad
upset
angry

If you were Mickey, what would you do? Why?

I would nep the girl

My Friends and Me

Friends are people we like to spend time with.   We can have a lot of things in common with our friends but we can also be very different.

A. **Draw your face and your friend's face in the circles. Fill in the chart.
Then answer the question.**

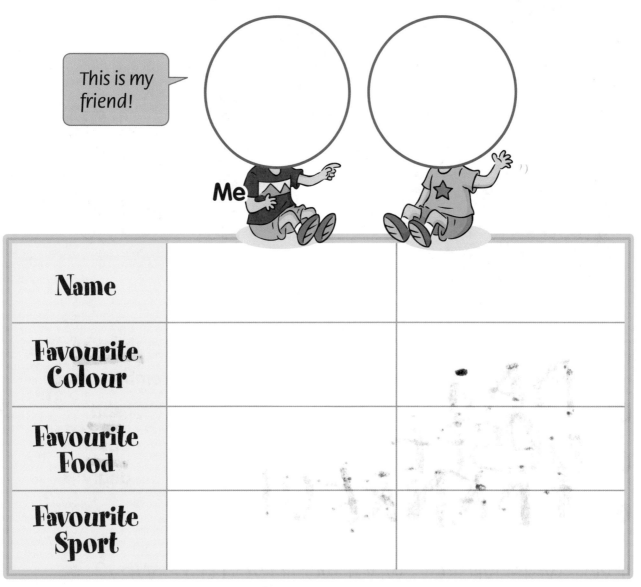

This is my friend!

Me

Name		
Favourite Colour		
Favourite Food		
Favourite Sport		

Things we like to do together:

_____

B. You and your friends have jobs at home and at school. Check ✔ the correct boxes to show what you and your friends do. Then share ideas with your friends.

At Home / At School	Me	My Friends	
		Name	Name
Help wash dishes			
Make the bed			
Help fold clothes			
Put away toys			
Show respect for others			
Help classmates			
Go to school on time			
Follow rules			

Share ideas with your friends on how to take more responsibilities at home and at school.

12

New Experiences

As we grow up, we have new experiences. Starting school for the first time is one of these experiences that brings us new feelings and responsibilities.

A. Think about your first day of school. Answer the questions.

1. How did you feel on your first day of school? Colour the faces.

2. If you felt nervous, did someone help you feel better? How?

_____ helped me feel better by

_____ .

3. Have you helped a new student feel better on his/her first day of school? How?

_____

_____

B. **Read what the children say. Then colour the faces and circle ⃝ the correct words.**

I played with other kindergarten children at the fenced playground during recess last year. This year, I can play in the entire school playground. It is awesome!

Doing homework is a new and good experience for me.

New Experiences in Grade 1

Having recess with other classes:

1. How you feel:

2. How to be responsible:

- **Do not go / Go** beyond the boundary.

- Play with the others **rudely / respectfully** .

Doing homework:

1. How you feel:

2. How to be responsible:

- **Keep up / Play** with your homework.

- Hand in homework **on time / late** .

13

Helping Others

We can all help one another. Sometimes adults help us. At other times, we help adults and other children. Helping others is a good way to show that we care.

A. Fill in the blanks to see how the people help others.

child

adult

senior

1.
An adult is helping a

_____ .

2.
A child is helping a

_____ .

3.
A child is helping an

_____ .

B.   Draw lines to show who can help in these situations.

driving children to
soccer practice

sharing school supplies
with a friend

setting the table

helping a child with
homework

Who Can Help?

a child

an adult

a senior

**C.   Write one thing you can do at home to help
your parents.**

Good
job!

_____

My Home

We each have a place we call home. Our home is part of a neighbourhood.

A. Describe your home. Then colour the pictures to show the buildings that you can find in your neighbourhood.

My Home

Check ✔ the home that looks like yours.

My home is:

big   small

cozy   cute

happy

I live with:

_____

_____

_____

My Neighbourhood

B. **Look at the map of Sally's neighbourhood. Give the map a title and answer the questions.**

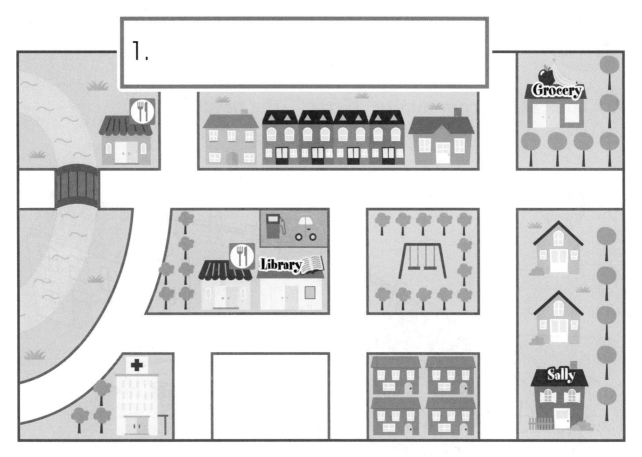

1.

2. Circle ⭕ the restaurants on the map.

3. If Sally and her family want to go to the closest restaurant, which one should they go to? Draw a line to take them there.

4. Is there anything in your neighbourhood that is missing in this neighbourhood? What is it?

_____

5. If you could add one thing new to this neighbourhood, what would it be? Draw it in the empty space on the map.

Nature around Me

We can find nature in our community. It provides us with fresh air and fun places to play in.

A. Look at this community. Circle ◯ the nature parts.

B. Read the riddles about fun places in nature. Match them with the correct areas. Write the letters. Then answer the question.

A I am protected from the sun while I read a book.

B My friends and I love to play a game of soccer here.

C In winter, this is my favourite place to toboggan.

Many things in nature are important to us. How would you feel if the tree was cut down or the park was replaced by buildings? Why?

_____

_____

My Local Community

A community is where we live, work, and play. The resources in our community help meet our daily needs.

A. Look at this community. Write the letters in the circles to answer the questions.

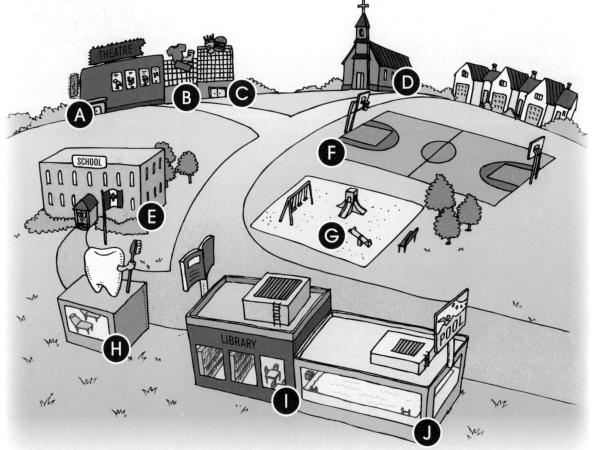

Where do you…

1. buy clothes? ◯

2. see a dentist? ◯

3. borrow books to read? ◯

4. play basketball? ◯

B. Look at the community. Answer the questions.

1. Rover Farm supplies produce such as vegetables and meat to some stores in this community. Circle ○ the stores.

2. The community wants to replace Rover Farm with a shopping mall. Read the comments from different people. Check ✔ the one that you agree with most and explain what you think.

"We will have a good place to shop." ○

"There will be fewer farm products to sell in the food stores." ○

"There will be less beautiful nature in the community." ○

Explain: _____

Community Workers

Many people work in a community. These workers provide services and products for everyone living in the community.

A. Match the community workers with their services. Write the letters.

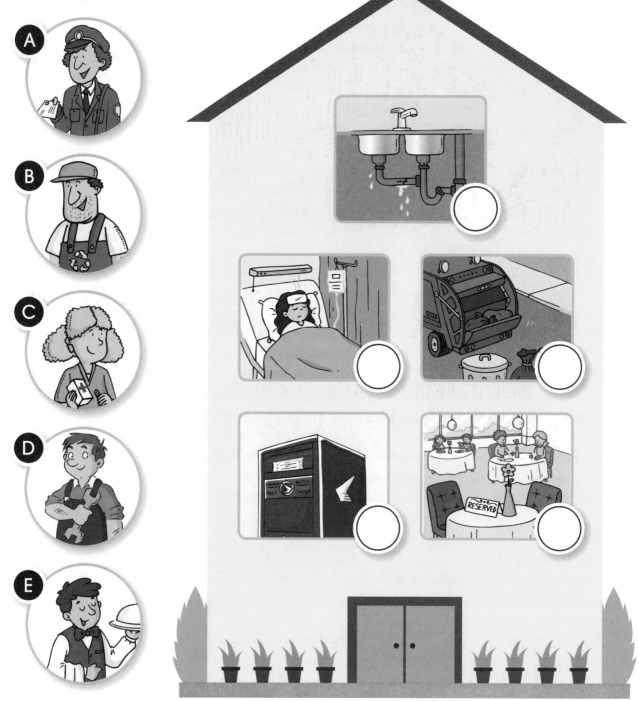

B. Many people help us every day in our school community. Complete the crossword puzzle to find out who they are.

SCHOOL

caretaker
bus driver
crossing guard
librarian teacher
coach principal

18

Helping My Community

We each can do our part to help out in our community. There are many things we can do to help at home, at school, at the park, and in other places in our community.

A. The children are going to clean things up. Draw lines to put the things in the correct bins.

At Home

At School

B. **Circle ◯ the things that need to be cleaned up at the park. Draw lines to put them in the correct bins. Then answer the questions.**

There are many things we can do to help our community.

Helping Our Community:

1. Join the **clean-up / mess-up** crew. Picking up trash in the neighbourhood helps keep our community neat and **quiet / tidy** .

2. **Donate / Sell** your outgrown clothes to a **shop / charity** . They will be given to kids in need.

19

People and Their Community

Every day, people affect their community by the choices and decisions they make. These actions have great effects on both the community and the environment.

A. See what Caleb is doing. Circle ○ the correct words and answer the question.

I'm full. I can't finish my sandwich.

Caleb

The effects of not using garbage cans:

- The park becomes **pretty / dirty** .

- Some **pests / pets** , such as rodents and flies, are drawn to the park.

- It creates more **work / fun** for park maintenance workers.

- The park is **clean / unsafe** to play in.

What should Caleb do with the leftovers to help keep the park clean?

_____

B. Read about the possible effects of turning a wooded area into a mall on Cali Town. Fill in the blanks and answer the question.

Plan: To Turn a Wooded Area into a Mall

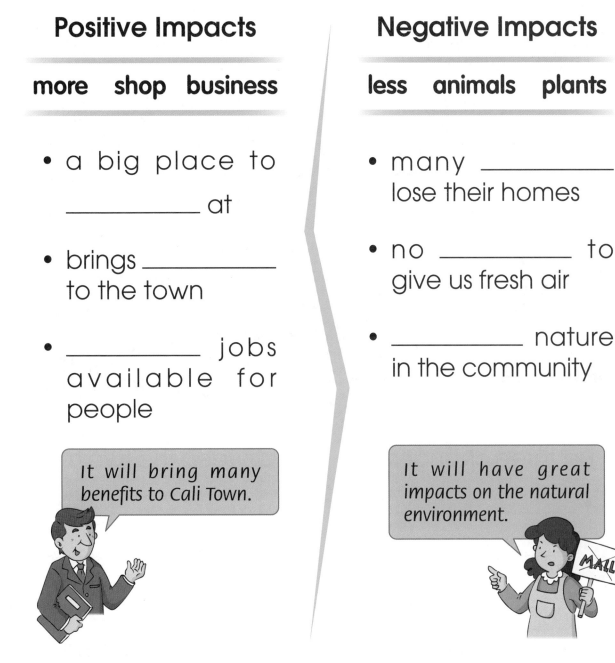

Positive Impacts

more   shop   business

- a big place to _____ at

- brings _____ to the town

- _____ jobs available for people

It will bring many benefits to Cali Town.

Negative Impacts

less   animals   plants

- many _____ lose their homes

- no _____ to give us fresh air

- _____ nature in the community

It will have great impacts on the natural environment.

MALL

Do you think it is a good idea to turn the wooded area in Cali Town into a mall?

_____

20

Community Changes

Our community is always changing. Changes may make our community a better place to live in.

A. **Look at the maps that show how a community has changed. Answer the questions.**

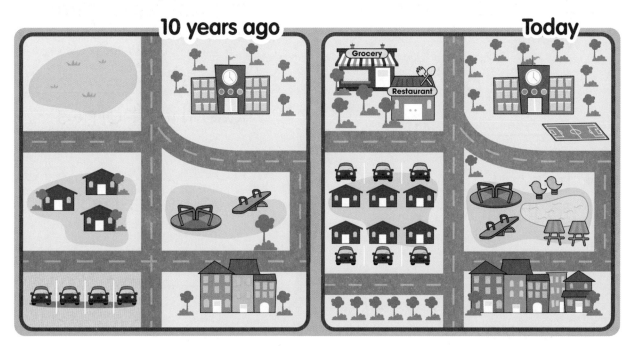

1. List three changes you see between the two maps.

   • _____

   • _____

   • _____

2. How did the changes help make the community a better place to live in?

   _____

B. Look at the pictograph of a tree-planting event. Answer the questions.

We feel great participating in this meaningful event. This is good for the community.

Leon

Trees Planted at York Park

Day	Number of Trees Planted
Day 1	🌳🌳🌳🌳🌳🌳🌳🌳
Day 2	🌳🌳🌳🌳🌳🌳🌳🌳🌳🌳
Day 3	🌳🌳🌳🌳🌳🌳🌳
Day 4	🌳🌳🌳🌳🌳🌳🌳🌳🌳🌳🌳🌳

1. How many trees were planted on

   • Day 1? _____   • Day 2? _____

   • Day 3? _____   • Day 4? _____

2. Which day had the most participants? Why do you think so?

   _____

   _____

3. Read what Leon says. Then check ✔ the reason why he says it.

   Ⓐ Trees will be cut to make paper.

   Ⓑ Trees will give people shade and fresh air.

4. Trees are not only good for us, they are also good for animals. Why?

   _____

Areas in the Community

A community is made up of different areas, each playing its part in serving the community.

A. Look at the community. Label the areas.

Residential for living	**Commercial** for working	**Recreational** for playing	**High Traffic** for travelling

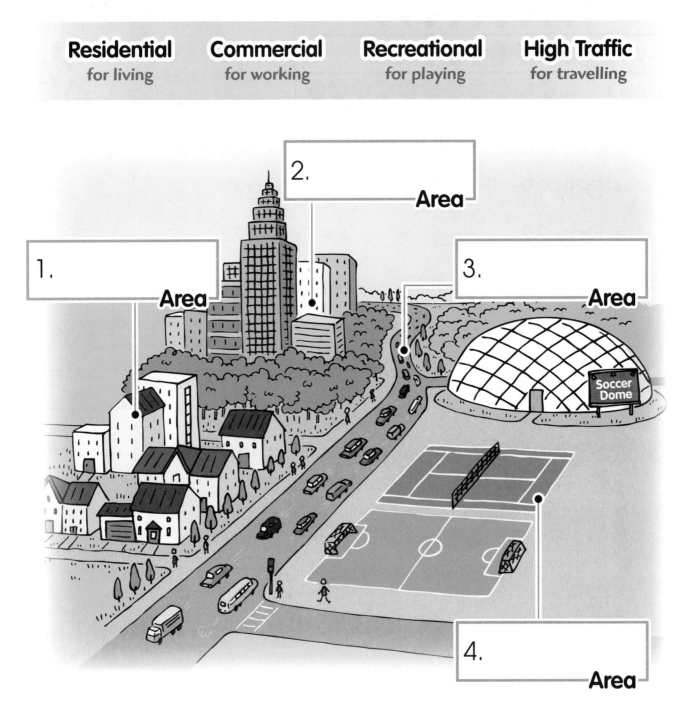

1. _____ Area

2. _____ Area

3. _____ Area

4. _____ Area

B.   Match the community areas with what you may find there.

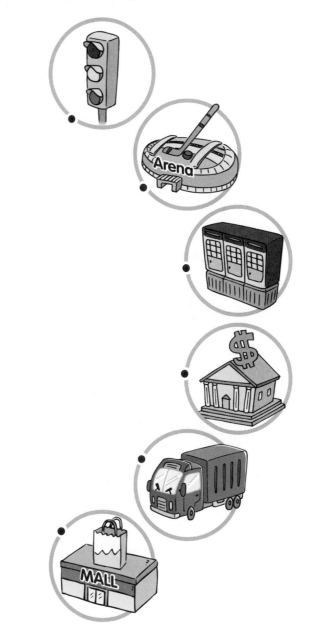

Residential area •

Commercial area •

Recreational area •

High Traffic area •

C.   Write about your favourite place in your community.

My favourite place in my community is _____

_____ .

It belongs to the _____ area.

Locating Places

We can describe the location of a place by using words that tell directions. Understanding directions is important in getting around our community.

A. Use the correct words to describe the locations and directions.

up   down   left   right   near   far   beside   across

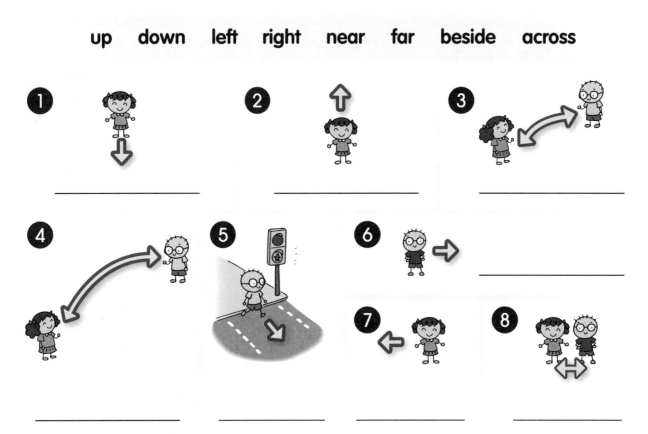

1 _____

2 _____

3 _____

4 _____

5 _____

6 _____

7 _____

8 _____

B. Fill in the blanks to take Jason to the park.

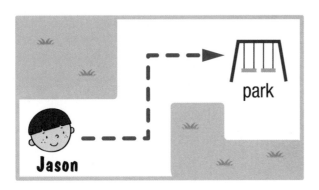

park

Jason

- Go _____ .

- Turn _____ and go up.

- Turn _____ and go to the park.

C. **Draw to complete the map. Then fill in the blanks and answer the question.**

near
far
left
right

1. The zoo is _____ from Rob's house.

2. The pet store is _____ the zoo.

3. The museum is to the _____ of the library.

4. Rob's house is to the _____ of the theatre.

5. Rob wants to go to the zoo. Draw a line with a red coloured pencil to show him the path.

go up → turn right → turn left → turn right →

There you are!

Using Maps

We use maps to show where places are in our community. We use symbols to represent places and things on maps. It is also important to know how to read the measurements on a map.

A. Choose the best symbols to complete the legend. Then colour and draw pictures on the map and answer the question.

Symbol Idea

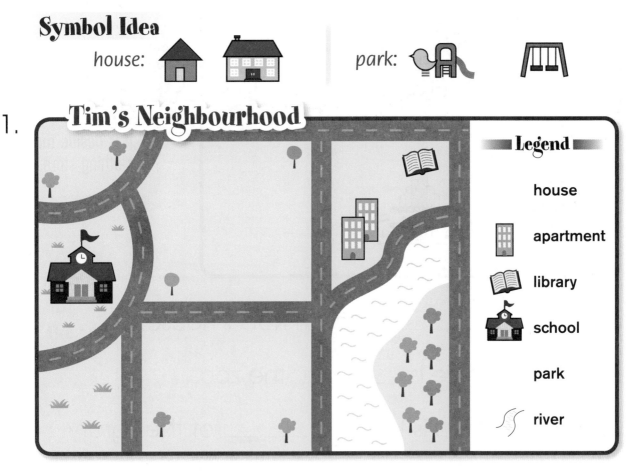

2. There are four houses and one park in Tim's neighbourhood. Draw them on the map.

3. Colour the river on the map. What colour would you use? Why?

B. Look at the floor plan. Answer the questions.

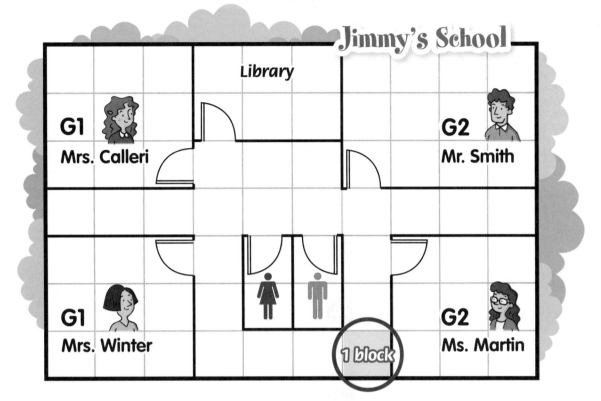

1. How many blocks are there in each classroom?

   Mrs. Calleri's classroom: _____ blocks

   Mr. Smith's classroom: _____ blocks

2. The two Grade 1 classrooms are _____ block(s) apart.

3.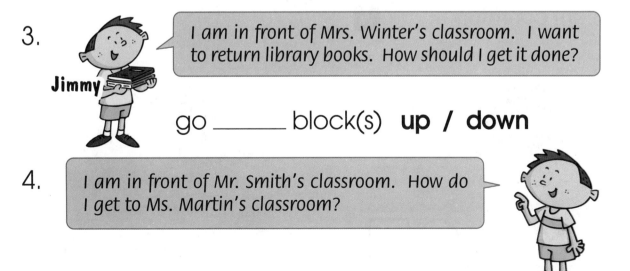

   I am in front of Mrs. Winter's classroom. I want to return library books. How should I get it done?

   Jimmy

   go _____ block(s) **up / down**

4. I am in front of Mr. Smith's classroom. How do I get to Ms. Martin's classroom?

   _____

Government Workers

The government helps our community through the services provided by its workers. These workers help keep us safe and healthy.

A. Identify the workers and their responsibilities. Write the letters in the correct places.

Workers

A doctor

B librarian

C firefighter

D police officer

E snowplough operator

F garbage collector

G park maintenance worker

H water treatment plant operator

Responsibilities

P makes sure roads are safe for driving when it snows

Q cares for trees and grass at parks

R puts books back on shelves

S helps us when we are sick

T makes sure that drivers obey traffic laws

U helps us in emergencies

V collects garbage

W makes sure water is safe for drinking

1.

2.

3.

 ◯ ☐

4.

 ◯ ☐

5.

B. **Read what Julie says. Then answer the question.**

In my community, we use clear garbage bags to keep our garbage collectors safe.

How should we dispose of broken glass to keep the garbage collectors safe from injury?

Julie

_____

_____

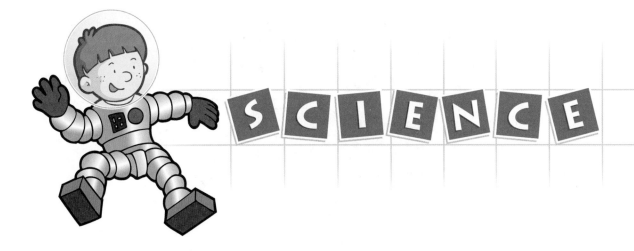

SCIENCE

My Body

- Our bodies have many useful parts.
- We use different parts of our bodies to do different things.

A. Fill in the missing letter for each part of the body.

fin**g**er

ar**m**

bac**k**

le**g**

foo**t**

Head

Chin

el**b**ow

h**a**nd

kne**e**

toe

B. Draw lines to match.

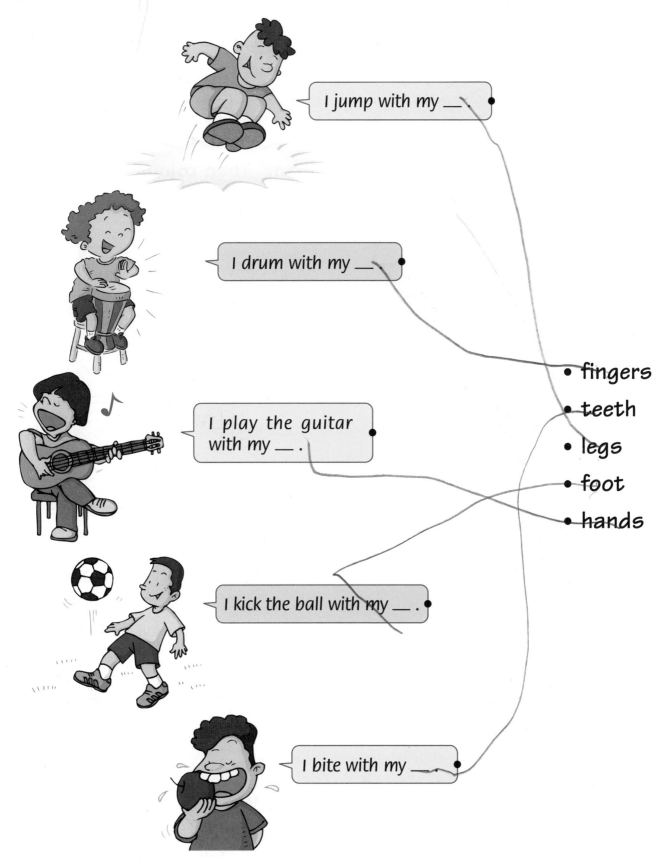

I jump with my __.

I drum with my __.

I play the guitar with my __.

I kick the ball with my __.

I bite with my __.

- fingers
- teeth
- legs
- foot
- hands

Five Senses

- Our bodies have sense organs: our nose, tongue, eyes, ears, and skin.
- With our sense organs we can smell, taste, see, hear, and touch.

A. Write the name of each sense organ.   Then colour the correct picture to tell what each sense organ can do.

ear
eye
nose
skin
tongue

EYE :

EAR :

NOSE :

TONGUE :

SKIN :

B. Complete the following rhymes with the given words.

hearing, ears touch, skin
taste, tongue smell, nose
sight, eyes

Apple pie or

Red red rose

For my sense of 1. SMELL

I use my 2. NOSE

Warm, soft kittens

Make me grin

For my sense of 5. TOUCH

I use my 6. SKIN

Ice cream here!

For old or young!

For my sense of 9. TASTE

I use my 10. TONGUE

Watching the puck or

The early sunrise

For my sense of 3. SIGHT

I use my 4. EYES

The sound of a hit

The crowd cheers

For my sense of 7. EARS

I use my 8. HEARING

Our Senses at Work

- Our senses tell us all about the world.
- Our senses keep us safe.
- Some things protect our sense organs.

A. Cross out ✗ the one that does not belong in each group.

1. **sense of hearing**

2. **sense of sight**

3. **sense of touch**

4. **sense of smell**

5. **sense of taste**

B. Write the correct sense(s) to know the things below.

see   hear   touch   smell   taste

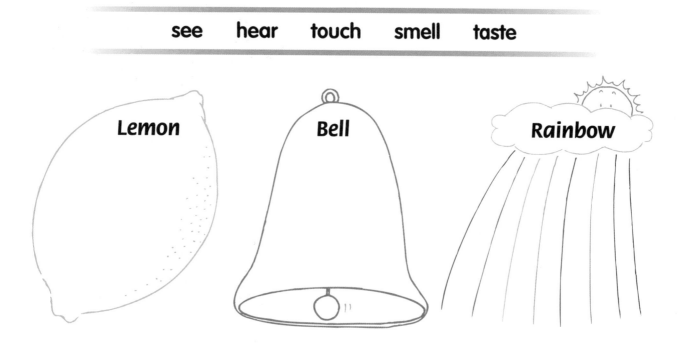

Lemon   Bell   Rainbow

C. Tell which group each item belongs to. Write the letters.

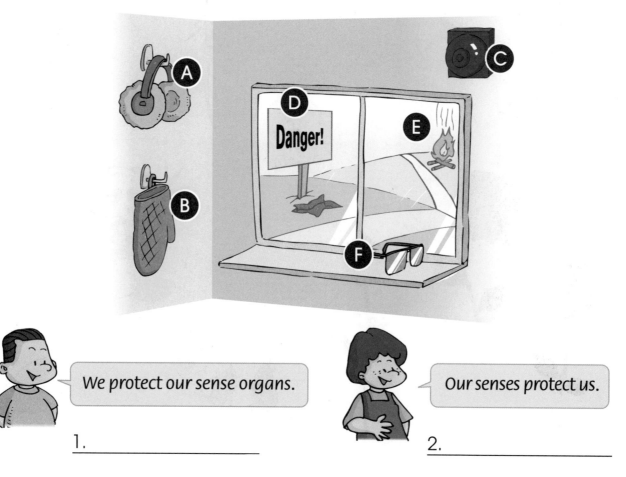

Danger!

We protect our sense organs.   Our senses protect us.

1. _____   2. _____

Living Things and Their Growth

- Living things grow and change.
- Living things reproduce, or have young.

I will grow bigger just like my mom.

A. **Show how living things grow. Put the pictures in order. Write 1, 2, and 3.**

1.

2.

3.

4.

B. Colour the living things in the picture.

5

Needs of Living Things

- Living things need air, water, and food.
- Living things have different ways of getting what they need to live.

A. Match the pictures with what the boy says. Write the letters.

A *We need the sun to make food.*

B

C

D

E

F

G

H

I

1. Living things need air. _____

2. Living things need water. _____

3. Living things need food. _____

B. **See what the living things get.   Fill in the blanks with "air", "water", or "food".**

 Fish get _____ through their gills.

 Plants get _____ through their roots.

 Salamanders can get _____ through their skin.

 Frogs catch _____ with their tongues.

 Camels can store large amounts of _____ .

 Plants make their own _____ with the help of the sun.

6

Living Things and the Way They Move

- Our bodies let us move in many different ways.
- The way animals move depends on their bodies.

A. Describe how the animals move with the given words.

hop   swing   gallop   slither   climb   dive   fly

1. _____

2. _____

3.

4. _____

5. _____

6. _____

7. _____

B. Describe the movements in the picture.

rolling   bouncing   throwing   diving   swinging

1.

2.

3.

4.

5.

Patterns in Living Things

- Patterns are things that repeat.
- Some living things have patterns.

Honey, don't you think we have beautiful patterns?

A. **Complete the patterns of the living things.   Then name the living things.**

tortoise   flower   bee   fish   pineapple   leaf

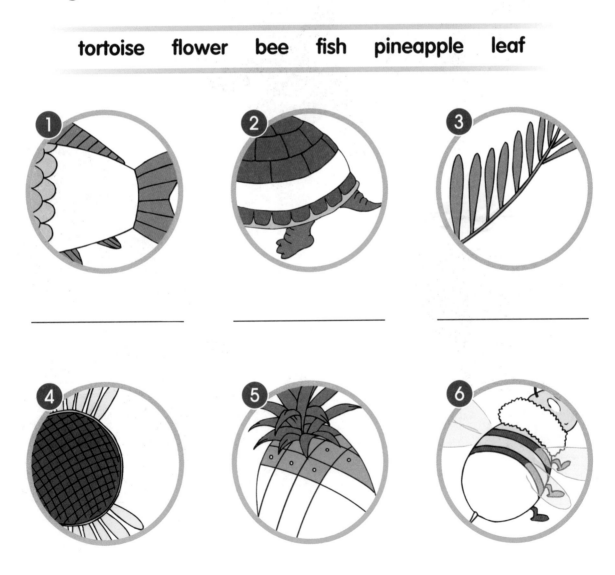

1 _____

2 _____

3 _____

4 _____

5 _____

6 _____

B. **Sort the living things by their patterns. Write the letters.**

spots: _____

rings: _____

spiral: _____

stripes: _____

Healthful Eating

8

- Canada's Food Guide helps us choose healthful food to eat.
- It is important to know where our food comes from.

Mom, which one is the best?

A. Look at the pictures. Sort them into the correct places. Write the letters.

Food Guide

Grain Products	Vegetables and Fruit	Milk and Alternatives	Meat and Alternatives
◯	◯	◯	◯
◯	◯	◯	◯
◯	◯	◯	
◯	◯		
◯			
◯			

Enjoy a variety of foods from each group every day.

B. Which food item is the most healthful choice in each group? Circle ◯ it and fill in the missing letters to complete its name.

1.

___uic___

2.

po___cor___

3.

fr___sh ___rui___

C. The highlighted pictures show where our food comes from. Cross out ✗ the food that does not belong.

9

Safe and Healthful Living

- There are things we can do to stay healthy: keep our bodies clean, exercise, and get plenty of sleep.
- Safety rules are important to know and follow.

A. Draw a line and colour the pictures to show David the path of healthful habits to reach the trophy.

David

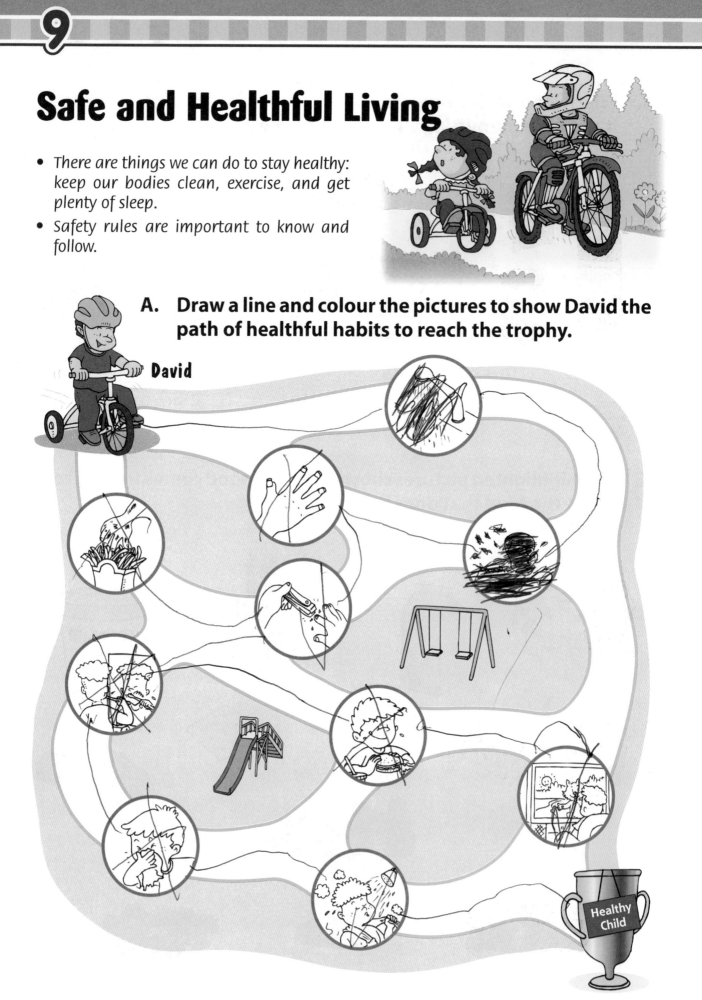

B. **Look at the pictures. Give the people the things they need to be safe. Write the letters.**

1.  B

2.  E

3.  A

4.  D

5.  C

6.  F

10

Objects and Materials

- Objects are things we can see and touch. Materials are the things that objects are made from.
- Different materials have different properties such as hardness and weight.

A. Colour the objects.

Objects made from
wood: brown
glass: blue
metal: yellow
cloth: green

B. Describe each object. Circle ◯ the correct word.

1.

hard soft

2.

light heavy

3.

rough smooth

4.

light
dark

5.

shiny dull

C. Cross out ✗ the material that cannot be used to make the given objects.

Shoe	Hard hat	Pillow
leather	glass	cloth
cement	metal	feathers
cloth	plastic	wood

11

Materials that Join

- *Some materials can be used to join things together.*

A. Colour the sheets with the names of materials that join things to help the little spiral find the paper.

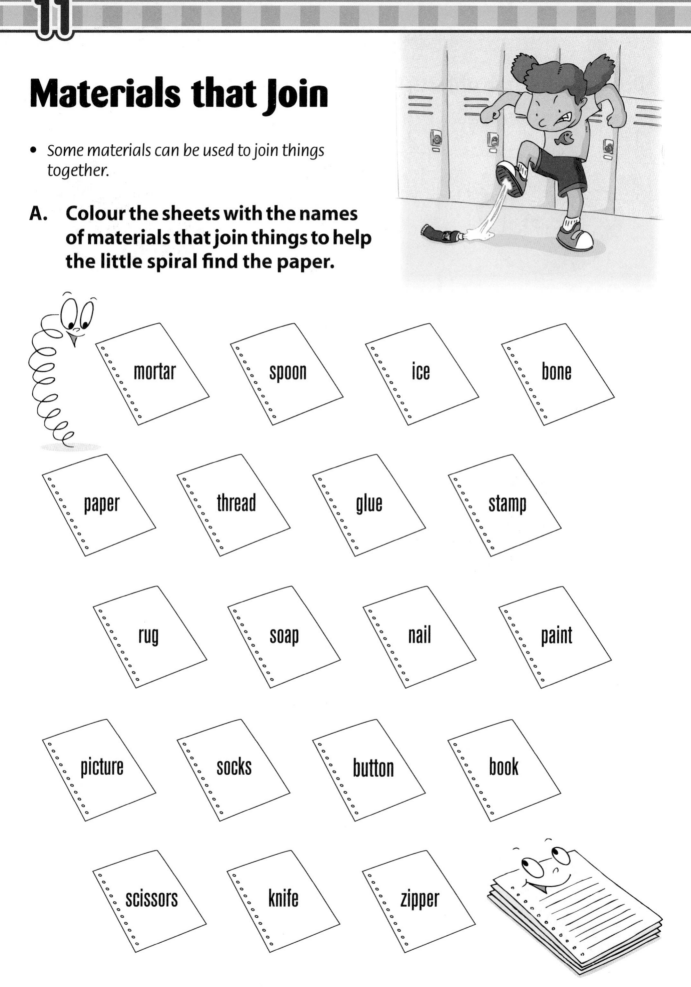

mortar

spoon

ice

bone

paper

thread

glue

stamp

rug

soap

nail

paint

picture

socks

button

book

scissors

knife

zipper

B. **Match the materials that need to be joined with the materials that will join them. Write the letters.**

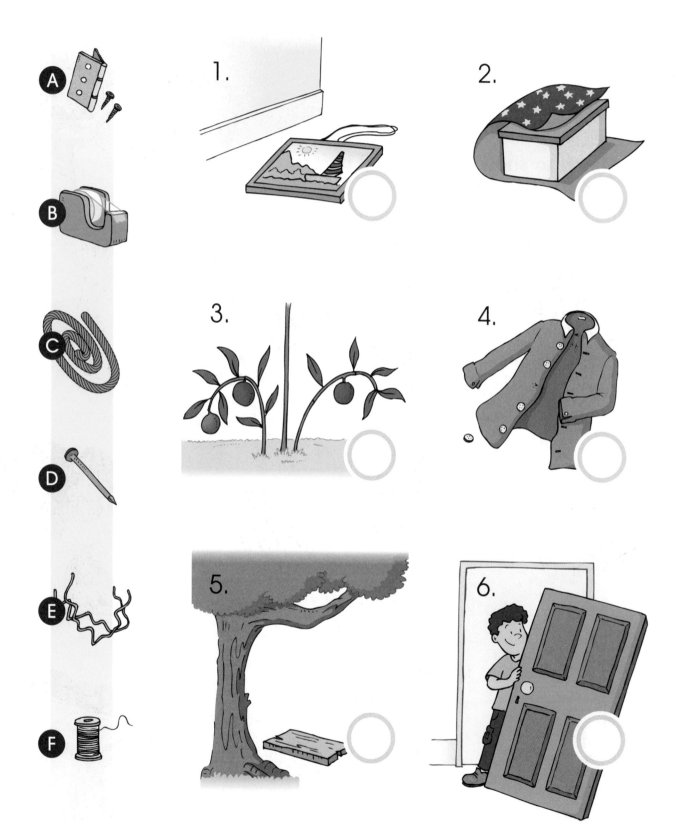

A

B

C

D

E

F

1.

2.

3.

4.

5.

6.

Changing Materials

- Heat, cold, and other things can change materials.
- When a material changes, some of its properties change.

A. Match to show the material before and after its change.

1.

2.

3.

4.

5.

6.

B. **Read what Dr. Stein says. Help him check ✔ the correct letters and fill in the blanks.**

thick   liquid
sticky   soft
runny   wet

Look at the change in each material. Tell whether the second one feels, smells, tastes, or looks different from the first one. Then describe the new properties of each material.

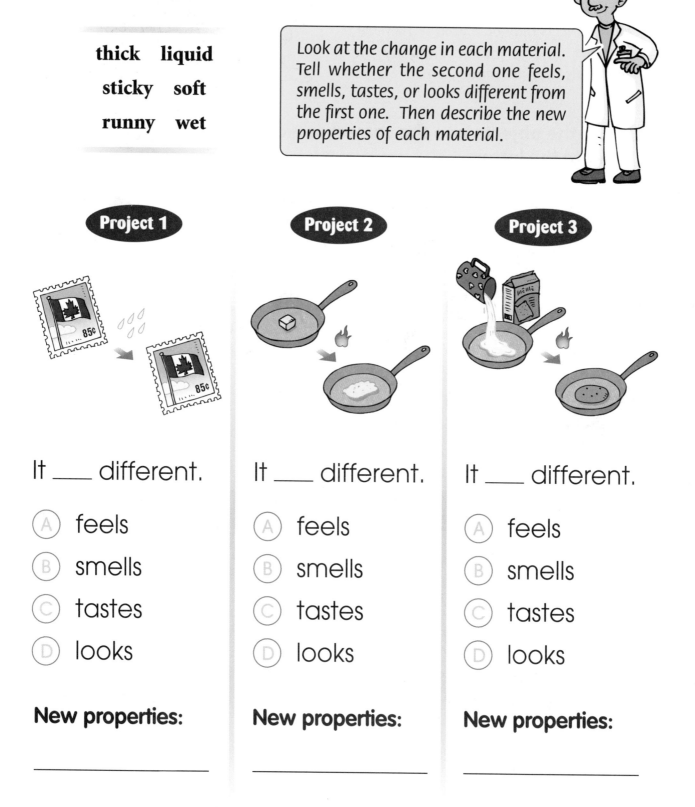

Project 1

It ___ different.

- Ⓐ feels
- Ⓑ smells
- Ⓒ tastes
- Ⓓ looks

New properties:

_____

_____

Project 2

It ___ different.

- Ⓐ feels
- Ⓑ smells
- Ⓒ tastes
- Ⓓ looks

New properties:

_____

_____

Project 3

It ___ different.

- Ⓐ feels
- Ⓑ smells
- Ⓒ tastes
- Ⓓ looks

New properties:

_____

_____

Reuse and Recycle

- Many objects may be reused or recycled.
- We sort objects for recycling by the materials they are made from.

A. Put the objects into the correct recycle bins. Write the letters.

 A
 B
 C
 D

 E
 F
 G
 H

 I
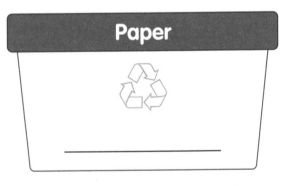 J
 K

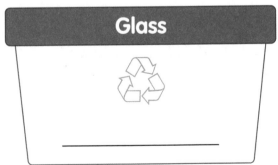

Paper	Aluminum
♻	♻
_____	_____

Glass	Plastic
♻	♻
_____	_____

B. Look at the picture. Colour the objects that are being reused or recycled.

C. How can each object be reused? Draw a picture.

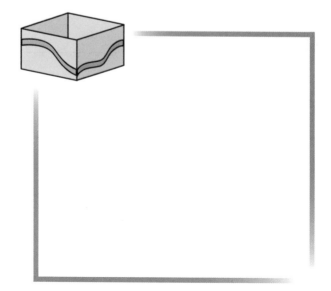

14 Energy and the Sun

- Energy makes things move or change.
- Most of the energy on Earth comes from the sun.

A. Help Sam write the words that the pictures stand for.

The 1._____ 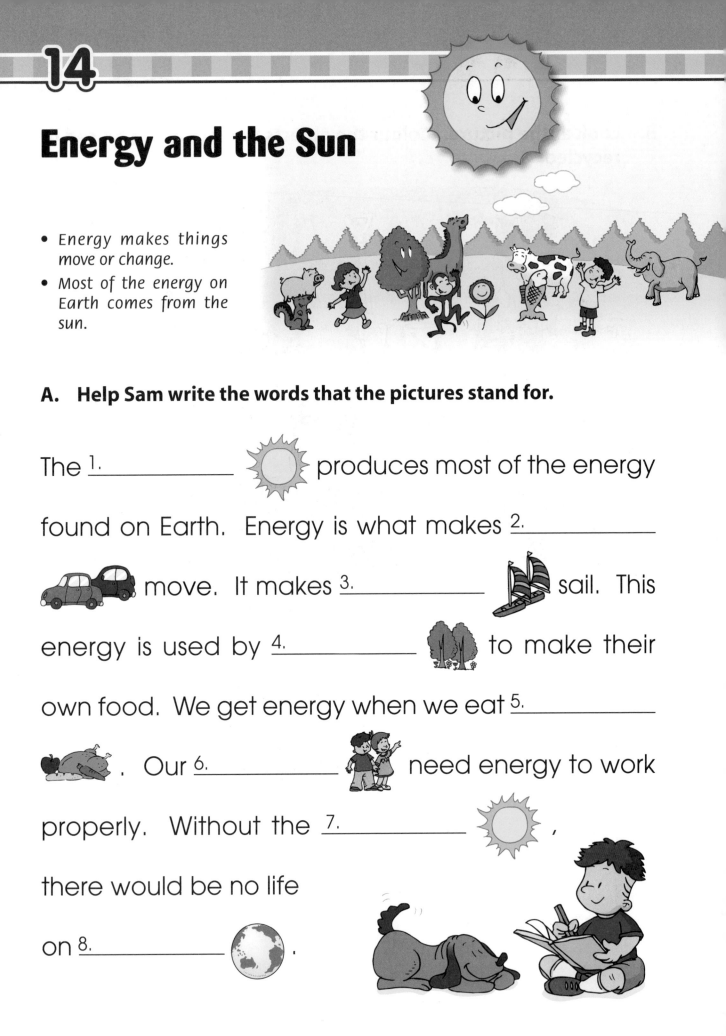 produces most of the energy found on Earth. Energy is what makes 2._____ move. It makes 3._____ sail. This energy is used by 4._____ to make their own food. We get energy when we eat 5._____. Our 6._____ need energy to work properly. Without the 7._____, there would be no life on 8._____.

B. Trace the dotted lines to complete the sun. Then colour the words related to the sun in the word search.

sun   life   energy
heat   light

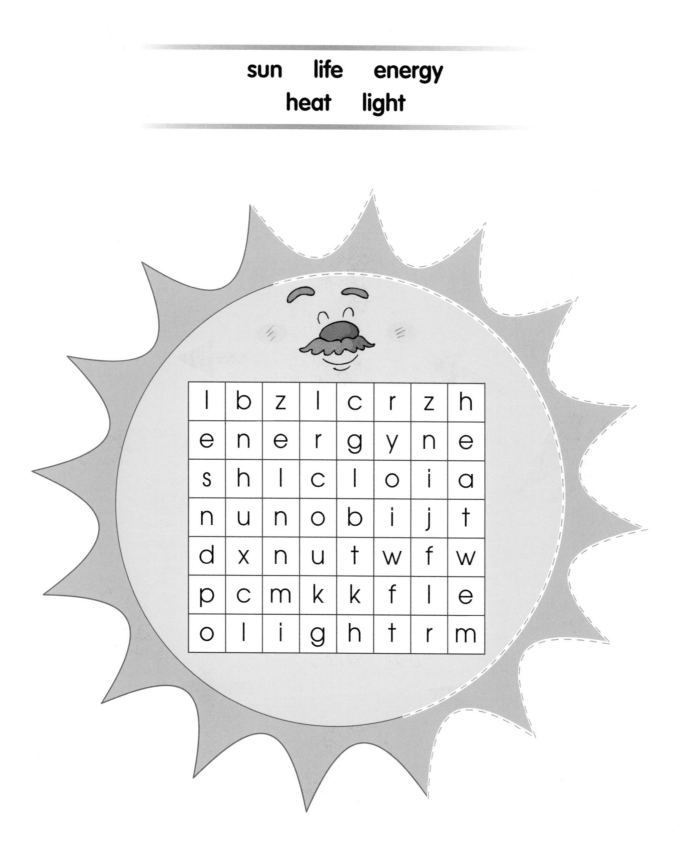

l	b	z	l	c	r	z	h
e	n	e	r	g	y	n	e
s	h	l	c	l	o	i	a
n	u	n	o	b	i	j	t
d	x	n	u	t	w	f	w
p	c	m	k	k	f	l	e
o	l	i	g	h	t	r	m

15

Energy and Food

- The sun provides energy for green plants and all other living things.
- We get energy to keep us active and alive by eating other living things.

A. Colour the correct pictures to show how the living things get energy.

> I get energy from food.

B. Complete the food chain with the given words.

lion   grasshopper   fox   grass

Food chain:

C. We need energy to do things every day. Put in order the following things done from the least amount of energy used to the greatest. Write the letters.

16

Smart Energy Use

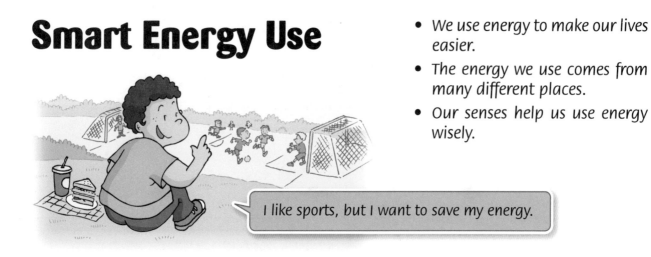

- We use energy to make our lives easier.
- The energy we use comes from many different places.
- Our senses help us use energy wisely.

I like sports, but I want to save my energy.

A. **Write the names of the energy givers in the pictures with the given words.**

| sun | electricity | wood | gasoline | wind |

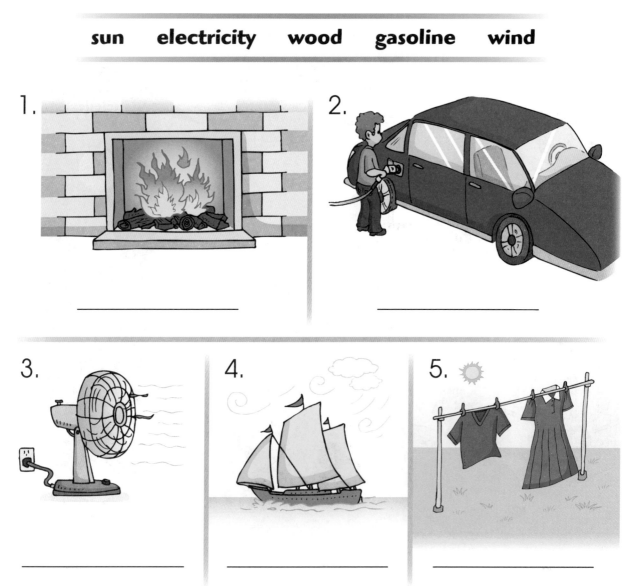

1. _____

2. _____

3. _____

4. _____

5. _____

B. **What senses do we use to tell ourselves when we need energy, or when to stop using energy? Write the senses on the lines.**

hearing   sight   touch

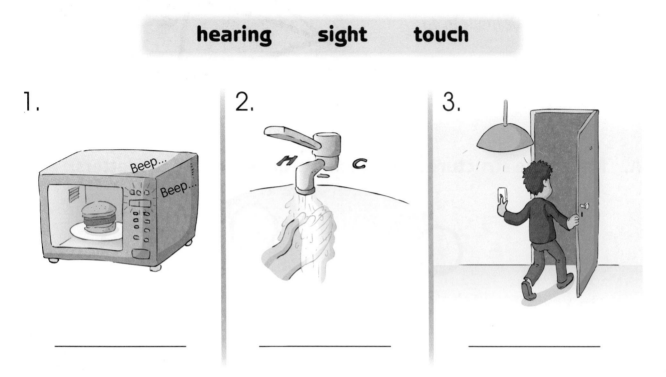

1.

2.

3.

_____   _____   _____

C. **Colour the scene that shows the wiser use of energy in each pair.**

17

Structures around Us

- Structures can be made to do things for us.
- Structures can be made from simple shapes.

A. Match the structures with their purposes. Write the letters.

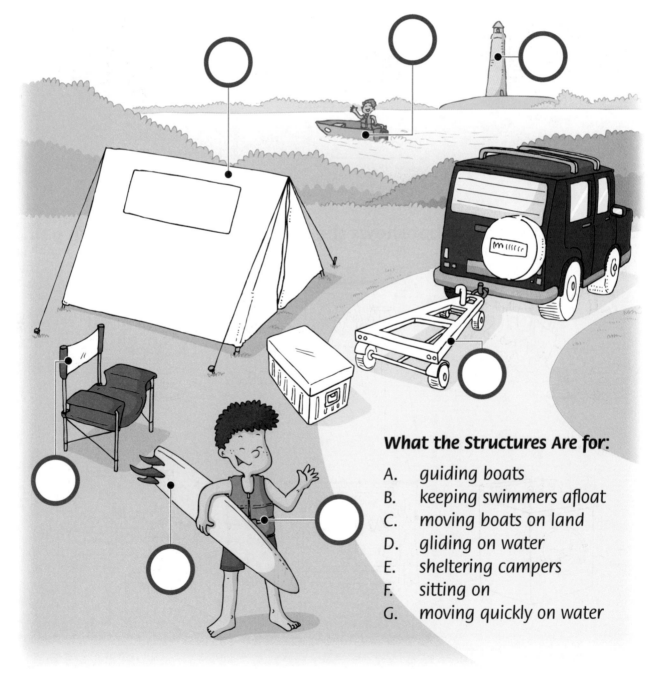

What the Structures Are for:

A. guiding boats
B. keeping swimmers afloat
C. moving boats on land
D. gliding on water
E. sheltering campers
F. sitting on
G. moving quickly on water

B. Name and colour the shapes. Then find an example of each shape in the camping scene on page 316 by colouring it with the same colour.

Rectangle – yellow　　**Circle** – orange　　**Triangle** – blue

1. _____ 　　 2. _____ 　　 3. _____

C. Connect the dots and write the names of the structures.

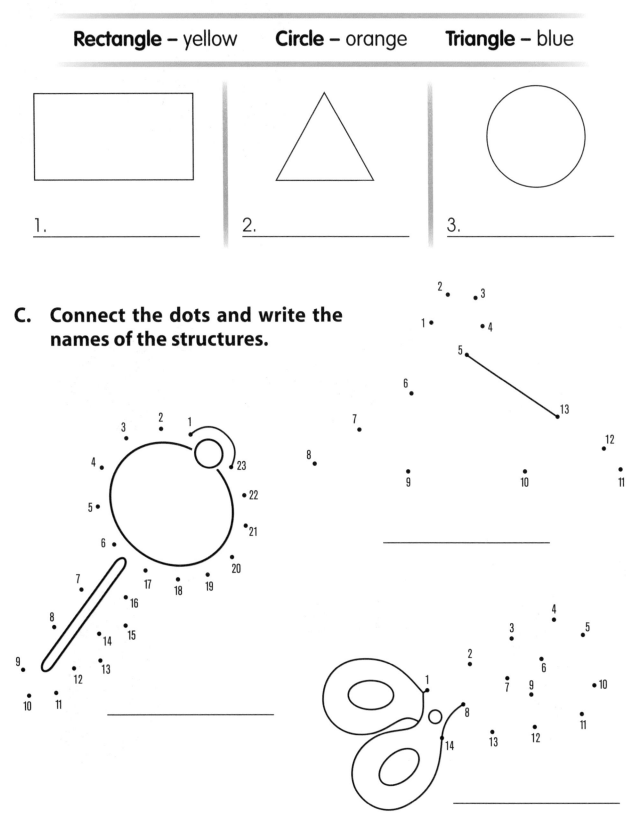

18

Natural Structures

- Living and non-living things produce structures.
- We see structures in the natural world and we create versions of our own based on them.

A. Match each structure with the correct builder. Write the letter.

A. spider   B. honeybee   C. robin   D. termite
E. woodpecker   F. freezing and thawing water

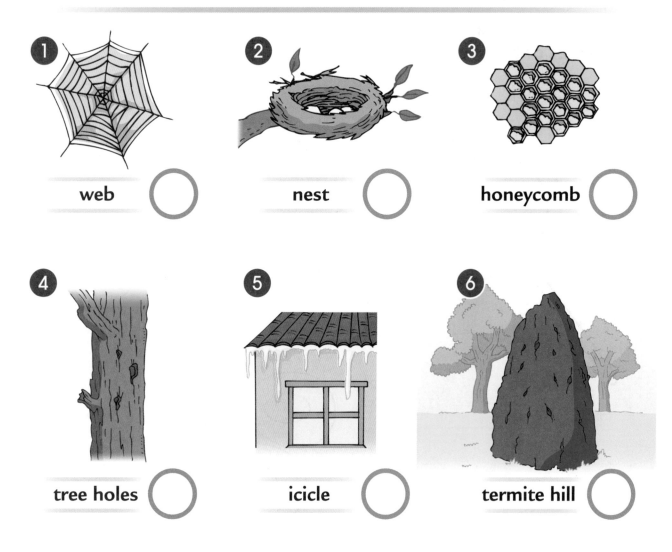

1. web ◯

2. nest ◯

3. honeycomb ◯

4. tree holes ◯

5. icicle ◯

6. termite hill ◯

B. **Write the names of the natural structures that are similar to the human constructions.**

spider web   beaver dam   honeycomb

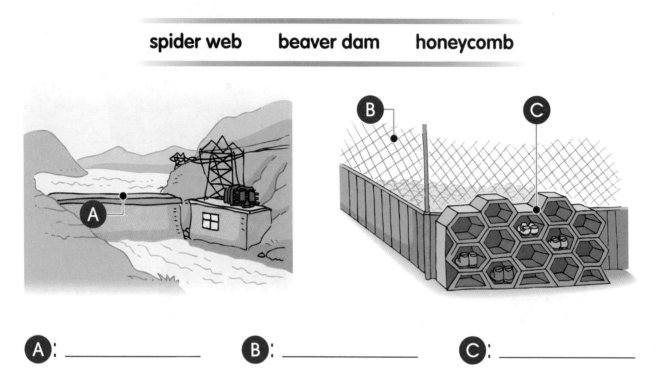

A: _____   B: _____   C: _____

C. **Match the structures found in our body with the jobs that they perform.**

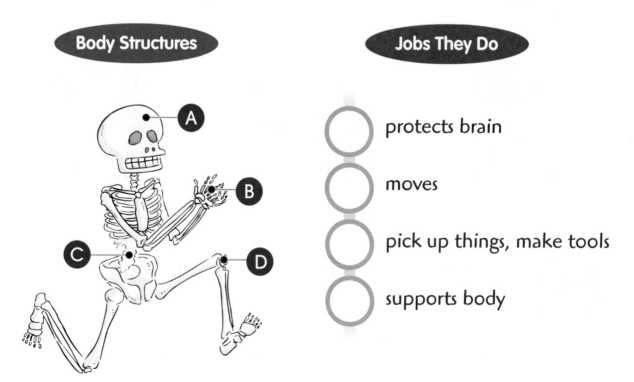

Body Structures

Jobs They Do

○ protects brain

○ moves

○ pick up things, make tools

○ supports body

Structures Together

A lock and a box make a safe.

- Two or more structures can be joined to make a device.
- A device can be used to help us.

A. Circle ◯ the structures that are needed to make each new device.

1.

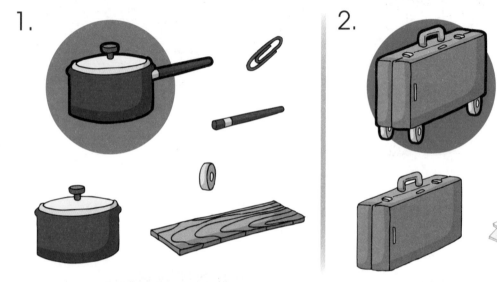

2.

3. 4. 5.

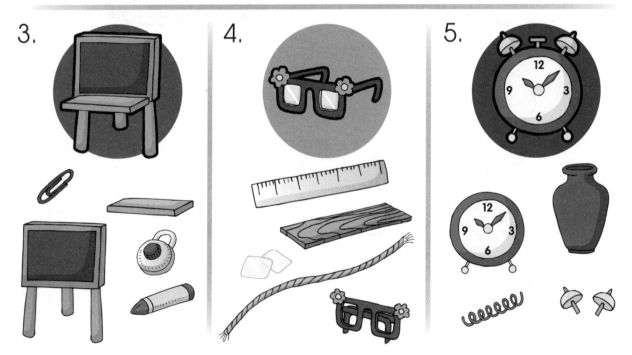

B. Look at Gabe's new device. Check ✔ the correct pictures to show what structures Gabe has used to build it.

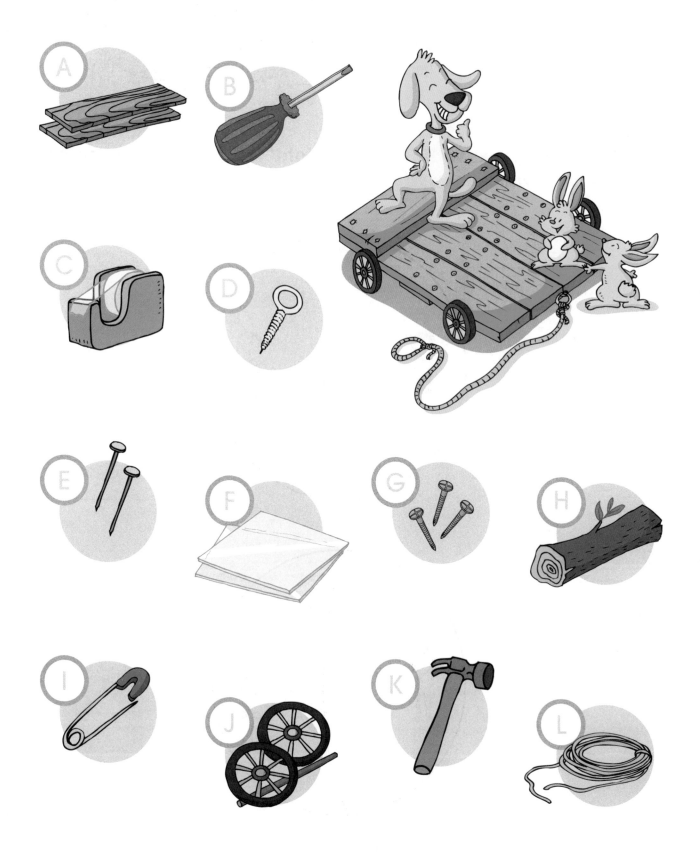

20

Day and Night

- The sun gives us light. The Earth rotates to give us day and night.
- Different things happen at different times of the day.

A. **Fill in the blanks with "day" or "night". Then colour the part of the Earth which shows day yellow and the part which shows night blue.**

1.

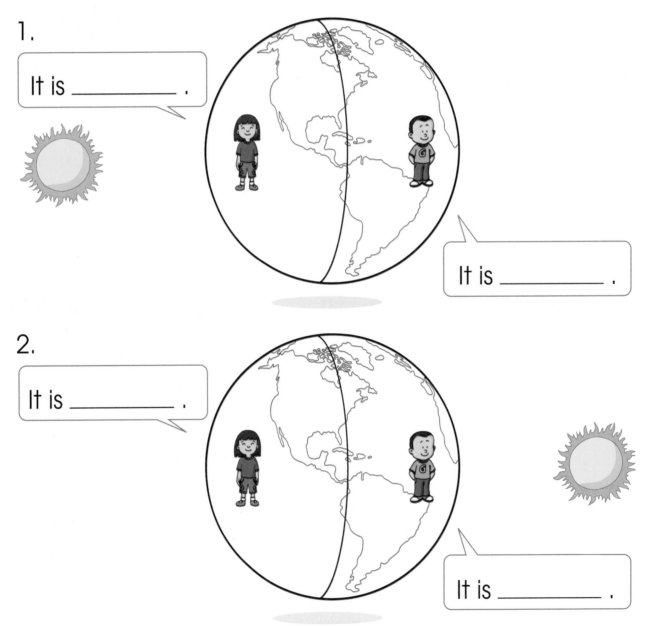

It is _____ .

It is _____ .

2.

It is _____ .

It is _____ .

B. **Check ✔ the picture that shows what happens next.**

1. A sunflower following the sun, shown at three different times of a day:

2. A child's daily routine:

C. **Match the shadows with the times of a day. Write the letters.**

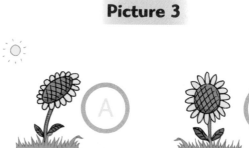

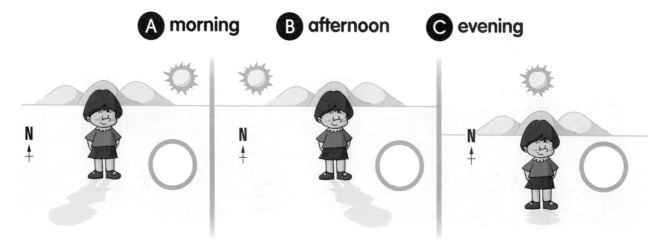

21

Seasons

- The four seasons are spring, summer, fall, and winter.
- The things we do depend on the season we are in.

A. **When do we do these activities?   Put them in the correct groups. Write the letters.**

Work

Play

Summer

Work: _____

Play: _____

Winter

Work: _____

Play: _____

B. **Fill in the missing letters to complete the name of each season. Then circle ◯ the picture that matches the season.**

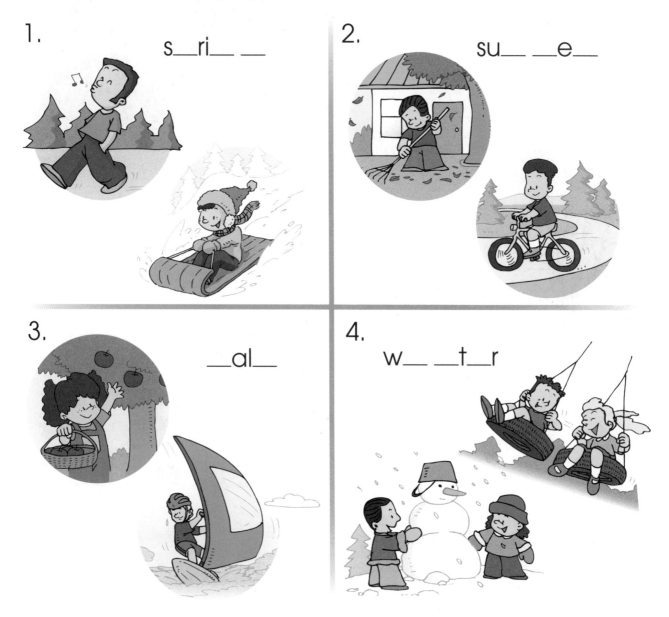

1.
s__ri__ __

2.
su__ __e__

3.
__al__

4.
w__ __t__r

C. **Answer the questions.**

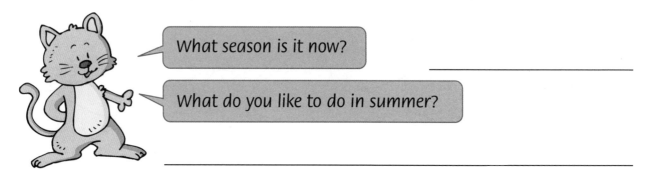

What season is it now?

_____

What do you like to do in summer?

_____

22

Plants through the Seasons

- *From season to season, we can see changes in many plants.*

A. Write the correct season for each picture.

1. _____

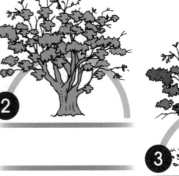

2. _____

3. _____

4. _____

B. Colour the maple leaves in different seasons.

1. Summer

2. Fall

C. Draw lines to match the plants in spring with the same plants in summer.

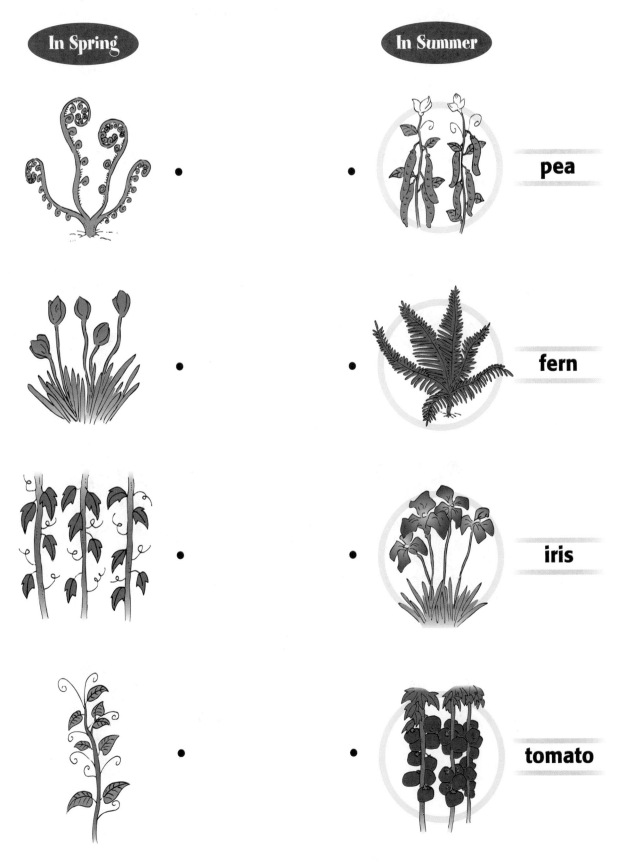

In Spring

In Summer

pea

fern

iris

tomato

Animals through the Seasons

- Animals change with the seasons.
- Animals have different ways of living through cold winters.

I will dress myself in a thick coat for the whole winter.

A. What seasons are the animals in? Write "spring", "summer", "fall", or "winter" on the lines.

1.

WINTER

2.

← South

FAll

3.

SUMMER

4.

SPRING

5.

FAll

6.

SPRING

B. See what the animals do to live through cold winters. Match the pictures with the descriptions. Write the letters.

(A) hibernate through cold winters

(B) migrate to warm homes in the south

(C) grow thick fur coats to help them stay warm

C. Read the poem. Write the season the animals are getting ready for.

Store your nuts, young squirrel.

Go to sleep, little snail.

Eat your salmon, black bear.

Go south, humpback whale.

FALL

Night Animals

- Some animals sleep in the day, and hunt and eat at night. They are nocturnal.
- Nocturnal animals have strong senses that help them live in the dark.

A. Colour the nocturnal animals. Then match the animals with their names. Write the letters beside them.

A. raccoon
B. firefly
C. skunk
D. cat
E. bat
F. owl
G. toad
H. grizzly bear

B. **Match the strong senses with the correct nocturnal animals. Circle ◯ the correct animals.**

1. **Sense of Hearing**

2. **Sense of Sight**

3. **Sense of Smell**

4. **Sense of Touch**

ANSWERS

1 Comparison

1.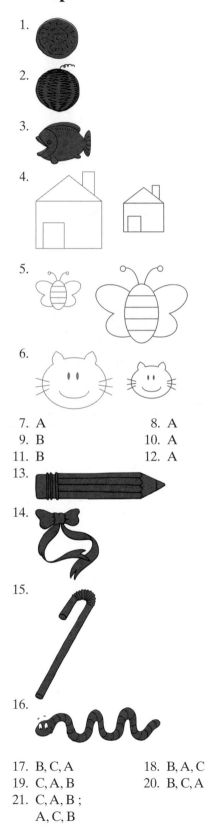

2.

3.

4.

5.

6.

7. A   8. A
9. B   10. A
11. B   12. A

13.

14.

15.

16.

17. B, C, A   18. B, A, C
19. C, A, B   20. B, C, A
21. C, A, B ;
    A, C, B

22. (Suggested answer for the longer bracelet)

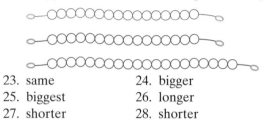

23. same   24. bigger
25. biggest   26. longer
27. shorter   28. shorter

2 More about Comparison

1.

2.

3.

4.

5.

6.

7.

8.

9.

10.

11.

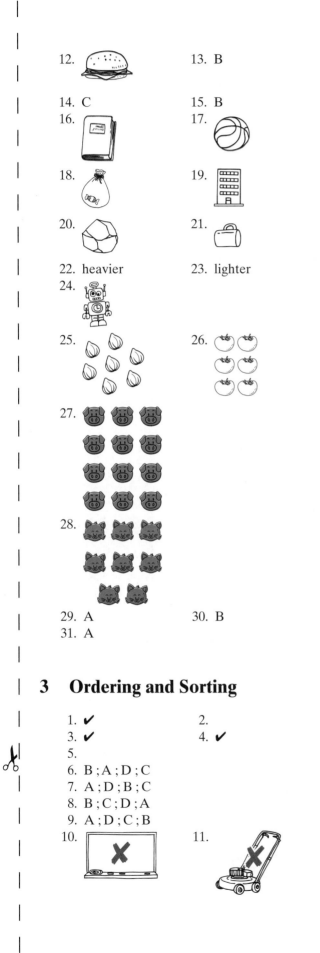

12. (hamburger) 13. B

14. C   15. B

16. (book)   17. (basketball)

18. (bag)   19. (building)

20. (rock)   21. (bag)

22. heavier   23. lighter

24. (robot)

25. (onions)   26. (tomatoes)

27. (pigs)

28. (cats)

29. A   30. B

31. A

3 Ordering and Sorting

1. ✔   2.

3. ✔   4. ✔

5.

6. B ; A ; D ; C

7. A ; D ; B ; C

8. B ; C ; D ; A

9. A ; D ; C ; B

10. (laptop with X)   11. (lawn mower with X)

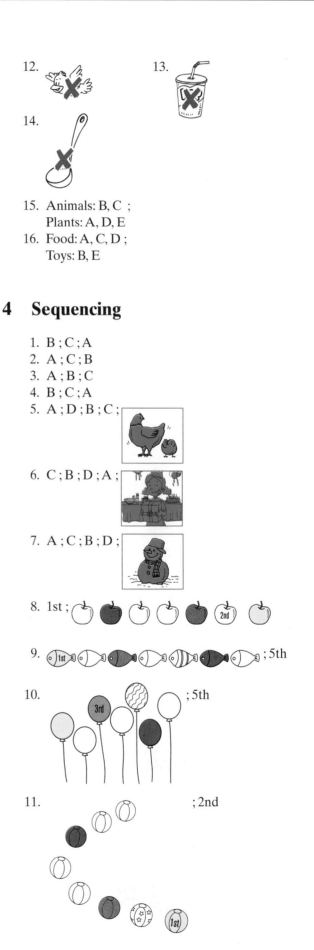

12. (bird with X)   13. (cup with X)

14. (ladle with X)

15. Animals: B, C ;
    Plants: A, D, E

16. Food: A, C, D ;
    Toys: B, E

4 Sequencing

1. B ; C ; A

2. A ; C ; B

3. A ; B ; C

4. B ; C ; A

5. A ; D ; B ; C ; (chicken and chick)

6. C ; B ; D ; A ; (person at table)

7. A ; C ; B ; D ; (snowman)

8. 1st ; (apples, 2nd marked)

9. (fish, 1st marked) ; 5th

10. (balloons, 3rd marked) ; 5th

11. (beach balls, 1st marked) ; 2nd

12. fifth 13. seventh
14. second 15. eighth
16. first 17. fourth
18. fourth ; third
19. first ; fourth ; sixth

5 Numbers 1 to 10

1. 3 2. 5
3. 6 4. 8
5. 2 6. 9
7. five 8. seven
9. six 10. eight
11. three 12. nine
13. 6 14. 10
15. 3 16. 8
17. 3 18. 6
19. 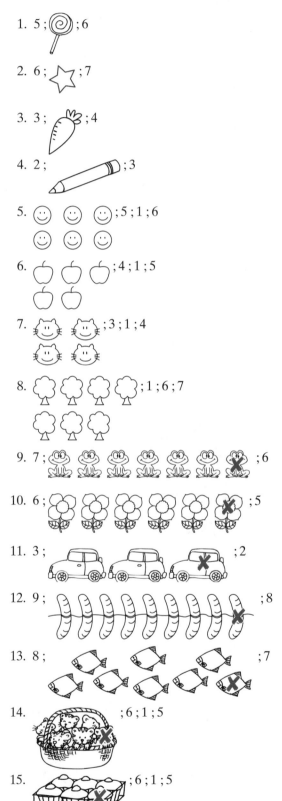 ; 4 20. ; 6
21. ; 5 22. ; 9
23.
24.
25.
26.
27. 3 ; 4 28. 6 ; 7
29. 5 ; 4 30. 8 ; 7
31. 6 ; 7 ; 8 32. 7 ; 6 ; 4
33. 7 ;

| 5 | 6 | **7** | 8 |

34. 3 ;

| **3** | **4** | 5 | 6 |

35. 3 ;

| 2 | **3** | 4 | 5 |

36. 9 ;

| 6 | 7 | **8** | **9** |

6 Addition and Subtraction of 1

1. 5 ; ; 6

2. 6 ; ; 7

3. 3 ; ; 4

4. 2 ; ; 3

5. ; 5 ; 1 ; 6

6. ; 4 ; 1 ; 5

7. ; 3 ; 1 ; 4

8. ; 1 ; 6 ; 7

9. 7 ; ; 6

10. 6 ; ; 5

11. 3 ; ; 2

12. 9 ; ; 8

13. 8 ; ; 7

14. ; 6 ; 1 ; 5

15. ; 6 ; 1 ; 5

16. 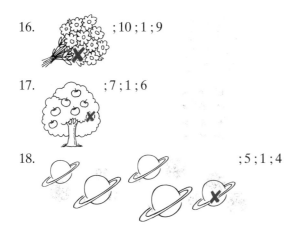 ; 10 ; 1 ; 9

17. ; 7 ; 1 ; 6

18. ; 5 ; 1 ; 4

7 Addition and Subtraction Facts to 6

1. ☀ ☀ ; 2 ; 5

2. ☺ ☺ ; 2 ; 4

3. ; 1 ; 5

4. 🐟 🐟 🐟 ; 3 ; 6

5. 2 ; 4   6. 4 ; 1 ; 5
7. 2 ; 1 ; 3   8. 3 ; 2 ; 5
9. 3 ; 1 ; 4   10. 2 ; 3 ; 5
11-12. (Individual drawings)
11. 6
12. 6
13.  ; 1 ; 2 ; 1 ; 2

14. ; 2 ; 2 ; 2 ; 2

15.  ; 3 ; 4 ; 3 ; 4

16. ; 1 ; 8 ; 1 ; 8

17. 3 ; 1 ; 4
18. 4 ; 1 ; 3
19. 5 ; 2 ; 3
20. 2 ; 3 ; 5

21. 2 ; 4 ; 6 ; 6
22. 3 ; 1 ; 2 ; 2

8 Addition and Subtraction Facts to 10

1. 5 ; 9   2. 5 ; 2 ; 7
3. 6 ; 3 ; 9   4. 2 ; 6 ; 8
5. 5 ; 2 ; 7   6. 4 ; 4 ; 8
7. 8   8. 6
9. 7   10. 10
11. 7   12. 9
13. 9   14. 5
15-24. (Draw 10 apples in the tree.)
15. 9   16. 4
17. 8   18. 8
19. 7   20. 10
21. 6   22. 6
23. 8   24. 7
25. 6 ; 2 ; 4   26. 5 ; 3 ; 2
27. 6 ; 5 ; 1   28. 9 ; 3 ; 6
29. 7 ; 3 ; 4   30. 8 ; 5 ; 3
31. 5   32. 3
33. 5   34. 2
35. 7   36. 4
37. 6   38. 4
39. 8   40. 3
41. 3   42. 8
43. 4   44. 10
45. 4   46. 9
47. 4
48. $\begin{array}{r} 10 \\ -\ 6 \\ \hline 4 \end{array}$; 4

9 More about Addition and Subtraction

1. 7   2. 8
3. 7   4. 4
5. 1   6. 3
7. 8   8. 3
9. 7   10. 2
11. 9   12. 7
13. 5   14. 5
15. 9   16. 2
17. 6   18. 5 ; 5
19. 7   20. 0 ; 3

21. 0 ; 4
22. 0 ; 5
23. 9
24. 8
25. 6
26. 1
27. 5
28. 4
29. 7
30. 3
31. 2
32. 0
33. 0
34. 0
35. 0
36. 0
37. 0
38. 0
39. 0
40. 0

41.
```
    2  ; 0
 -  2
    0
```

42.
```
    5  ; 0
 -  5
    0
```

43. 5 + 2 = 7 ; 7
44. 7 – 3 = 4 ; 4
45. 4 + 4 = 8 ; 8
46. 5 – 5 = 0 ; 0

10 Numbers 1 to 20

1. 6
2. 8
3. 16
4. 14
5. 15
6. 12
7. 16
8. 13
9. 20
10. 14
11. 11
12. 17
13. 8
14. 16
15. 11
16. 15
17. 9
18. 4
19. 14 ; 15 ; 16 ; 18
20. 17 ; 16 ; 14 ; 13
21. 9 ; 10 ; 12 ; 13
22. 7 ; 6 ; 4 ; 3
23. 12 ; 13 ; 14 ; 16
24. 14 ; 13 ; 12 ; 10
25. 5, 9, 13
26. 2, 10, 16
27. 4, 5, 8, 10
28. 2, 3, 7, 11
29. 12 ;

```
  11  12  13  14  15  16  17
```

30. 15 ;

```
  8  9  10  11  12  13  14  15  16
```

31. 8 ;

```
  8  9  10  11  12  13  14  15
```

32. 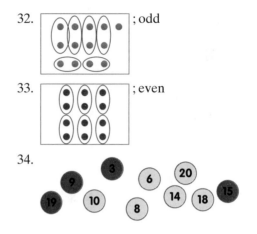 ; odd

33. ; even

34.

11 Numbers 21 to 100

1. 48
2. 37
3. 53
4. 66
5.

1	2	3	4	5	6	7	8	9	10
11	12	13	14	15	16	17	18	19	20
21	22	23	24	25	26	27	28	29	30
31	32	33	34	35	36	37	38	39	40
41	42	43	44	45	46	47	48	49	50
51	52	53	54	55	56	57	58	59	60
61	62	63	64	65	66	67	68	69	70
71	72	73	74	75	76	77	78	79	80
81	82	83	84	85	86	87	88	89	90
91	92	93	94	95	96	97	98	99	100

6. 57
7. 73
8. 90
9. 93
10. 66
11. 39
12. 66 ; 67 ; 70 ; 71
13. 90 ; 92 ; 93 ; 95
14. 42 ; 40 ; 39 ; 38
15. | Tens | Ones | ; 4 ; 7 ; 40 ; 7
    | 4 | 7 |

16. | Tens | Ones | ; 5 ; 2 ; 50 ; 2
    | 5 | 2 |

17. 6 ; 5
18. 10
19. 3 ; 8
20. 6
21. 9 ; 7
22. 80 ; 7
23. 53
24. 34
25. 49
26. 61
27. 54
28. 85
29. 23
30. 88 ;

```
  87  88  89  90  91  92
```

31. 31 ;
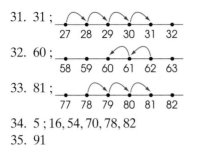

32. 60 ;

33. 81 ;

34. 5 ; 16, 54, 70, 78, 82
35. 91

12 Counting by 1's, 2's, 5's, and 10's

1. 87 ; 88 ; 90 ; 91 ; 92
2. 10 ; 9 ; 7 ; 6 ; 4
3. 17 ; 15 ; 14 ; 12 ; 11
4. 66 ; 67 ; 69 ; 70 ; 71
5. 47, 48, 49, 50, 51, 52, 53, 54, 55, 56, 57, 58
6. 16, 15, 14, 13, 12, 11, 10, 9, 8, 7, 6
7.

    2 ; 4 ; 6 ; 8 ; 10 ; 12 ; 14 ; 16 ; 16
8.

    2, 4, 6, 8, 10, 12, 14 ; 14
9.

    2, 4, 6, 8, 10, 12, 14, 16, 18 ; 18
10. 6
11. 8
12. 18
13. 16
14. 80 ; 82 ; 84 ; 88
15. 30 ; 28 ; 24 ; 22
16. a. 5   b. 10
    c. 15   d. 20
    e. 25   f. 30
    g. 35   h. 40
    i. 45   j. 50
17. 35 ; 45 ; 50 ; 60
18. 70 ; 75 ; 85 ; 95
19. 70 ; 65 ; 60 ; 50
20. 20 ; 25 ; 35 ; 40
21.

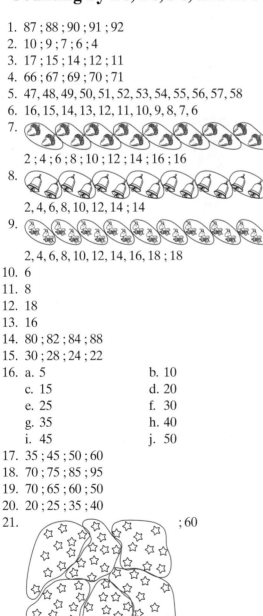

    ; 60

22.

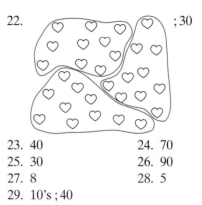

    ; 30

23. 40   24. 70
25. 30   26. 90
27. 8   28. 5
29. 10's ; 40

13 Money

1.

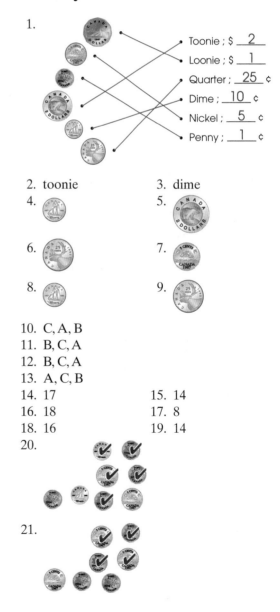

    Toonie ; $ 2
    Loonie ; $ 1
    Quarter ; 25 ¢
    Dime ; 10 ¢
    Nickel ; 5 ¢
    Penny ; 1 ¢

2. toonie   3. dime
4.   5.

6.   7.

8.   9.

10. C, A, B
11. B, C, A
12. B, C, A
13. A, C, B
14. 17   15. 14
16. 18   17. 8
18. 16   19. 14
20.

21.

22.

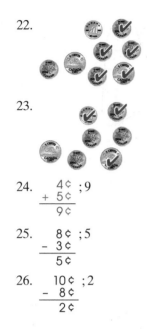

23.

24.
$$\begin{array}{r} 4\,¢ \\ +\ 5\,¢ \\ \hline 9\,¢ \end{array}$$
; 9

25.
$$\begin{array}{r} 8\,¢ \\ -\ 3\,¢ \\ \hline 5\,¢ \end{array}$$
; 5

26.
$$\begin{array}{r} 10\,¢ \\ -\ 8\,¢ \\ \hline 2\,¢ \end{array}$$
; 2

14 Measuring with Non-standard Units

1. 5 ; 15
2. 6 ; 18
3. 3 ; 9
4. 1 ; 3
5.

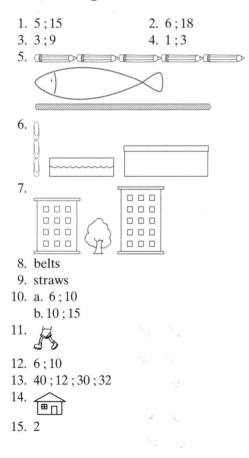

6.

7.

8. belts
9. straws
10. a. 6 ; 10
    b. 10 ; 15
11.
12. 6 ; 10
13. 40 ; 12 ; 30 ; 32
14.
15. 2

16. 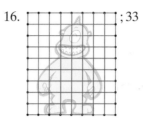 ; 33

15 Capacity

1. 2.

3. 4.

5.  6.

7.

8. a. more   b. the same capacity
9. a. less   b.
10. a. 7 ; 9   b. 2
11. a. 6   b. 1 ; 3
    c. more   d. 9
12. B   13. A
14. A   15. B
16. 8

16 Mass

1.  2.

3. 1 ; 2 ; 3
4. 2 ; 3 ; 1
5. 1 ; 3 ; 2
6.

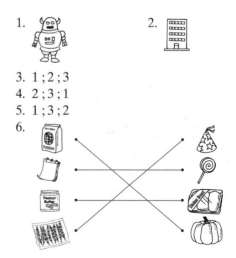

7. a. heavier
   b. lighter
8. a. heavier
   b. lighter
9. a. 10   b. 8
   c. 7   d. 5
10. house
11. doll
12.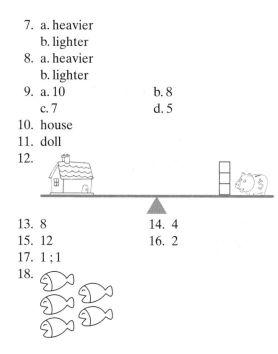
13. 8   14. 4
15. 12   16. 2
17. 1 ; 1
18.

9. 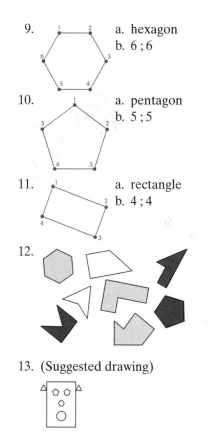 a. hexagon
                          b. 6 ; 6

10.   a. pentagon
                          b. 5 ; 5

11.   a. rectangle
                          b. 4 ; 4

12.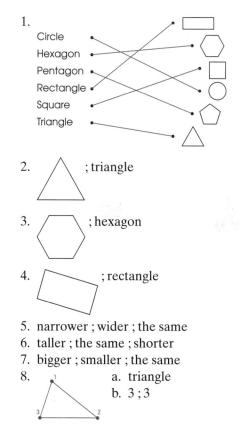

13. (Suggested drawing)

17 2-D Shapes

1.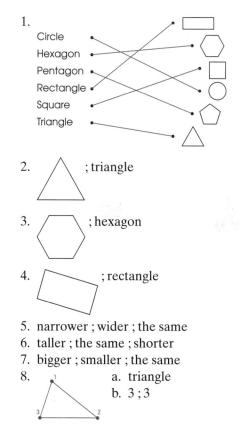
   Circle
   Hexagon
   Pentagon
   Rectangle
   Square
   Triangle

2. ; triangle

3. ; hexagon

4. ; rectangle

5. narrower ; wider ; the same
6. taller ; the same ; shorter
7. bigger ; smaller ; the same
8.   a. triangle
            b. 3 ; 3

18 More about Shapes

1.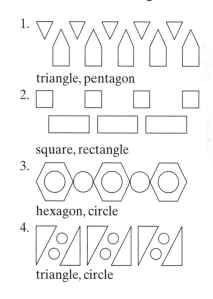
   triangle, pentagon
2.
   square, rectangle
3.
   hexagon, circle
4.
   triangle, circle

5.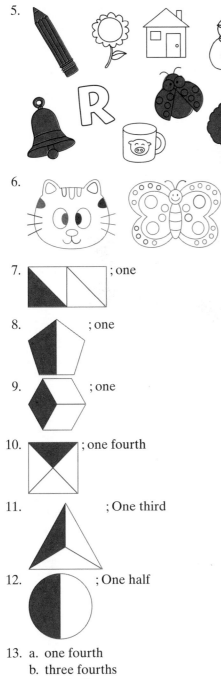

6.

7. ; one

8. ; one

9. ; one

10. ; one fourth

11. ; One third

12. ; One half

13. a. one fourth
    b. three fourths
14. a. one half
    b. one half
15. a. two thirds
    b. one third
16. No, because the sword is not in four equal parts.

19 3-D Solids

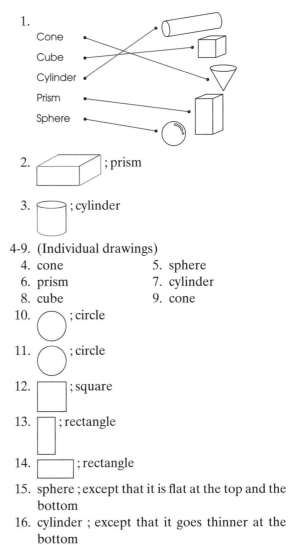

1.
Cone
Cube
Cylinder
Prism
Sphere

2. ; prism

3. ; cylinder

4-9. (Individual drawings)
    4. cone   5. sphere
    6. prism   7. cylinder
    8. cube   9. cone

10. ; circle

11. ; circle

12. ; square

13. ; rectangle

14. ; rectangle

15. sphere ; except that it is flat at the top and the bottom
16. cylinder ; except that it goes thinner at the bottom
17. cube ; except that it has four short legs at the bottom
18.

20 Directions (1)

1. Eric   2. Bill
3. in front of   4. behind
5. 2   6. 2
7. a. C   b. in front of
   c. behind
8. a. B   b. in front of
   c. in front of
9. a. right   b. left
   c. right

10. a. left   b. left
    c. right
11.

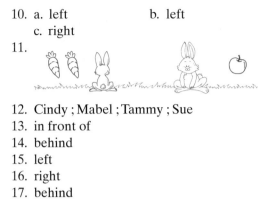

12. Cindy ; Mabel ; Tammy ; Sue
13. in front of
14. behind
15. left
16. right
17. behind
18. right
19. left

21 Directions (2)

1. a. inside   b. outside
2. a. outside   b. inside
3. a. inside   b. outside
4. a. under   b. over
    c. under   d. under
    e. under   f. over
    g-h.

5. Colour picture C. ; under
6. Colour picture A. ; over
7. Colour picture B. ; inside
8. inside
9. over
10. over
11. over
12. inside
13. There are 4 stars over the head of the clown.
14. The mouse is inside the hole.

22 Temperatures

1. Spring: B, G
   Summer: D, F
   Fall: C, E
   Winter: A, H
2. a. winter ; 4
    b. spring ; 1
    c. fall ; 3
    d. summer ; 2
3. [icon] ; sunny ; warm ;
    [icon] ; sunny ; hottest ;
    [icon] ; cold ;
    [icon] ; snowy ; coldest
4. low ; B
5. high ; hotter ; A
6. getting warmer
7. getting colder
8. 16 ; mild
9. 8 ; cold
10. 30 ; hot
11. 2 ; cold
12. 27 ; [thermometer showing 30 °C scale]

23 Days, Weeks, Months, and Time

1. Wednesday
2. Sunday ; Saturday
3. 3
4. Friday
5. playing on the computer
6. 7
7. 5 ; 9 ; 7 ;
   6 ; 10 ; 2 ;
   3 ; 12 ; 1 ;
   4 ; 11 ; 8

8.

OCTOBER							
	SUN	MON	TUE	WED	THU	FRI	SAT
		1	2	3	④	5	6
	7	8	9	10	11	12	13
		15	16	17	18	19	20
	21	22	23	24	25	26	27
	28	29	30				

○ Field Trip

9. Monday
10. October 4th
11. October 14th
12. October 29th
13. A: 7 ; 7
    B: 2 o'clock ; 2:00
    C: 9 o'clock ; 9:00
    D: 10 o'clock ; 10:00
14. A ; C ; B ; D
15. nearly ; 9 ; a little after 4 o'clock ; a little after half past 11

16.   17.

18.   19.

20.   21.

22.

24 Patterns

1. ✔   2. ✘
3. ✔   4. ✘
5. ✔
6. 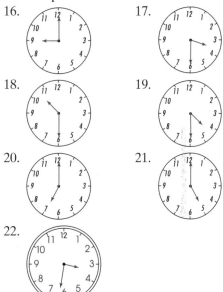   7.
8.   9.
10.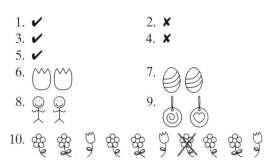

11.
12.
13-14. (Individual designs)
13.   14.
15.

16.

1	2	3	4	5	6	7	8	9	10
11	12	13	14	15	16	17	18	19	20
21	22	23	24	25	26	27	28	29	30
31	32	33	34	35	36	37	38	39	40
41	42	43	44	45	46	47	48	49	50
51	52	53	54	55	56	57	58	59	60
61	62	63	64	65	66	67	68	69	70
71	72	73	74	75	76	77	78	79	80
81	82	83	84	85	86	87	88	89	90
91	92	93	94	95	96	97	98	99	100

17. There is a 5 in the ones place.

25 Organizing Data

1. A: Apple: 15
       Orange: 20
   B: Big: 18
       Small: 17
2. A: Plant: ||||| ||
   B: Circle: ||||| |||||
       Square: ||||| ||||
3.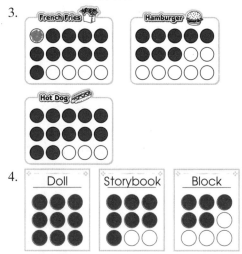
4.
5. dolls

26 Pictographs

1. fewer
2. fewer
3. 3
4. 4
5. 5
6. 4
7. 3
8. 2
9. basketball
10. 3
11. skating
12.

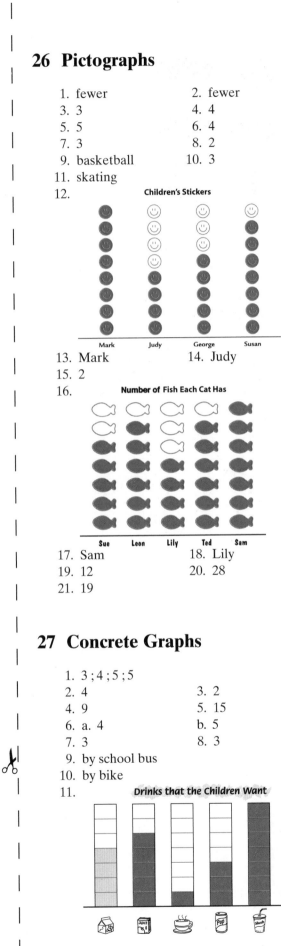

Children's Stickers

Mark   Judy   George   Susan

13. Mark
14. Judy
15. 2
16.

Number of Fish Each Cat Has

Sue   Leon   Lily   Ted   Sam

17. Sam
18. Lily
19. 12
20. 28
21. 19

27 Concrete Graphs

1. 3 ; 4 ; 5 ; 5
2. 4
3. 2
4. 9
5. 15
6. a. 4
b. 5
7. 3
8. 3
9. by school bus
10. by bike
11.

Drinks that the Children Want

12. a. 5
b. 4
13. 24
14. In summer, because almost all the children wanted cold drinks.
15.

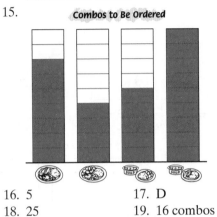

Combos to Be Ordered

16. 5
17. D
18. 25
19. 16 combos

28 Probability

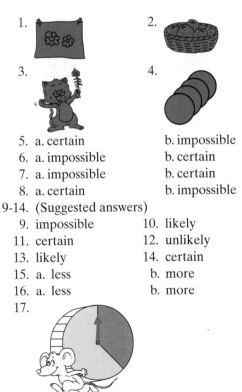

1.
2.
3.
4.
5. a. certain
b. impossible
6. a. impossible
b. certain
7. a. impossible
b. certain
8. a. certain
b. impossible
9-14. (Suggested answers)
9. impossible
10. likely
11. certain
12. unlikely
13. likely
14. certain
15. a. less
b. more
16. a. less
b. more
17.

1 A Visit to a Petting Farm

A. 1. countryside
    2. animals
    3. milk
    4. ponies
    5. patch
    6. sweet

B.

b	h	k	l	e	n	q	i	a	o	u	m	d
p	a	n	i	m	a	l	s	v	l	p	i	c
d	i	s	n	w	z	p	y	g	x	o	l	q
k	c	z	b	j	v	a	h	o	w	n	k	m
g	t	c	o	u	n	t	r	y	s	i	d	e
n	p	m	g	y	j	c	w	e	r	e	i	k
f	a	r	o	u	x	h	l	j	p	s	t	h
e	h	i	c	s	w	e	e	t	d	m	b	f

C. 1. p
    2. f
    3. s
    4. b
    5. w
    6. h

D. 1. g
    2. d
    3. b
    4. c
    5. t
    6. p
    7. r
    8. p

2 Over the Ocean Blue

A. 1. sailboat
    2. ocean liner
    3. kayak
    4. canoe

B. 1. ✔
    2.
    3. ✔
    4.
    5. ✔
    6. ✔

C. 1.
    2.
    3.

D.

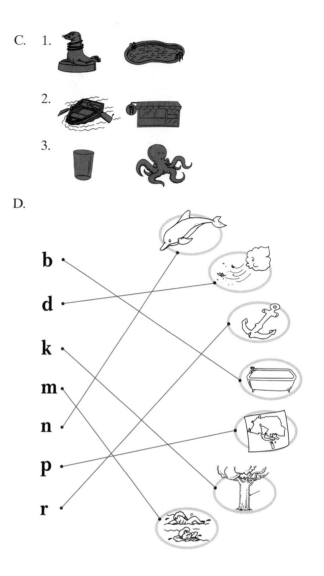

3 The Story of the Greedy Dog

A. 1. sad
    2. wide
    3. new
    4. opened
    5. big
    6. take

B. 1. No
    2. Yes
    3. Yes
    4. No
    5. Yes

C.

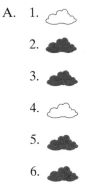
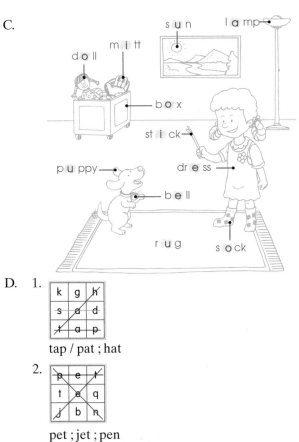

d **o** ll   m **i** tt   s **u** n   l **a** mp

b **o** x

st **i** ck

p **u** ppy   dr **e** ss

b **e** ll

r **u** g   s **o** ck

D. 1.

tap / pat ; hat

2.

pet ; jet ; pen

3.

big ; bib ; him

4.

mop ; dog / god ; fox

5.

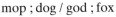

sun ; cup ; bug

6.

bit ; bag ; hut

4 Sometimes We Just Like to Look at the Sky...

A. 1.
2.
3.
4.
5.
6.

B. (Individual drawing and writing)
C. 1. a ; a ; a ; a
2. o ; o ; o ; o ; o
3. u ; u ; u ; u
4. i ; i ; i ; i

D.

5 Variety – the Spice of Life

A. Food: sushi ; dim sum ; stew ; apple pie
Taste: sour ; salty ; sweet ; spicy
B. (Suggested answers)
1-syllable word: eat
2-syllable word: apple
3-syllable word: cucumber
4-syllable word: jambalaya

C.

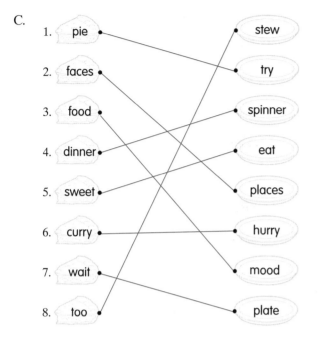

1. pie — try
2. faces — places
3. food — eat
4. dinner — spinner
5. sweet — plate
6. curry — hurry
7. wait — stew
8. too — mood

D. (Colour these words.)
1. thicken
2. bushy
3. meat
4. handle
5. bye
6. bees

6 A Chant from Ghana

A. 3 ; 5 ; 1 ; 2 ; 4
B. (Individual writing and drawing)
C.

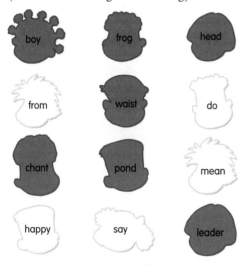

boy   frog   head
from   waist   do
chant   pond   mean
happy   say   leader

D. 1. girl ; pool
2. fish ; water
3. weather
4. sun ; sky
5. children ; schoolyard
E. (Individual drawing and writing)

7 A Letter to a New Friend

A. 1. Choco
2. Emi
3. Greg
4. Hugh
5. Kiyoka
6. Mandy
7. Sammy
B. 1. Sammy
2. Japan
3. pen pal
4. Samantha
5. Emi
C.

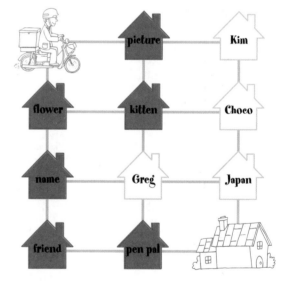

picture   Kim
flower   kitten   Choco
name   Greg   Japan
friend   pen pal

D. Person: brother ; cousin ; teacher
Animal: dog ; bird ; horse
Place: school ; farm ; park
Thing: letter ; picture ; cap

8 A Letter from Japan

A. 1. Hana
2. Kiyoka
3. Kenichi
4. Keiko
5. Pekko

B. 1.
2. ✔
3.
4. ✔
5. ✔

C. 1. Sammy ; Canada
2. Miss Wilson ; Kiyoka ; English
3. Japan
4. Japanese
5. The Lion King
6. Simba
7. Lakeside School
8. Toronto
9. Pekko

D. (Answers will vary.)
1. Jose likes playing with me.
2. I feed Puffy every morning.
3. My cousin works in Barrie.
4. He is reading *The Brave Heart*.
5. Miss Wilson is the best teacher in my school.
6. Ottawa is a nice place to visit.

9 Our Chores

A. 6 ; 3 ; 5 ;
4 ; 1 ; 2

B. (Individual drawing and writing)

C. 1. beds
2. flower
3. school
4. plants
5. houses
6. mug
7. bowls
8. book
9. parents

D. 1. mop
2. towel
3. sink
4. plates
5. cups

6. balls
7. apples
8. cat
9. boy

10 Mr. Mom

A. 2 ; 1 ; 5 ; 3 ; 4

B. (Individual drawing and answer)

C. 1.
2.
3.
4.
5.
6.
7.
8.
9.

D. 1. C
2. B
3. E
4. D
5. A

E. (Individual writing)

11 Perogies

A.
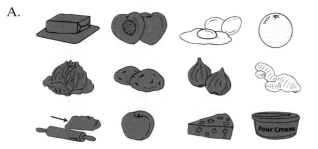

B. 1. Many
    2. fill
    3. like / love
    4. great
C. 1. ✔
    2. ✔
    3.
    4. ✔
    5.
    6.
D. 1. I like perogies.
    2. Tony loves toast with jam.
    3. Ice cream is Kim's favourite.
    4. We all enjoy eating perogies.
E. (Individual drawing and writing)

12 The Sun and the Wind

A. 1. r ; heavy
    2. i ; strong
    3. k ; smiled
    4. e ; bright
    5. p ; forehead
B. 1. park
    2. heavy coat
    3. hard
    4. handkerchief
C. 1. No
    2. Yes
    3. Yes
    4. No
    5. Yes
    6. No
    7. Yes
D. 1. Is it cold in the fall?
    2. Do you like fluffy snow?
    3. Why is the winter so long?
    4. Who likes snowy days?
    5. What can we do in winter?
    6. When will the snow stop?
E. 1. Is it windy outside?
    2. Do you have a thicker coat?
    3. Where are you going?
    4. Are you coming with me?

13 Duck Hunting

A. 1. A
    2. B
    3. A
    4. A
    5. B
B. (Individual writing)
C. 1.
    2.
    3.
    4.
    5.
    6.
    7.
    8.
D. Too bad!
E. 1. What a narrow escape!
    2. Dear me!
    3. You won't believe it!
    4. How bad the hunters are!

14 I Like Winter

A. 1. fall
    2. spring
    3. winter
    4. summer
B. (Individual writing)
C. 1. canada ; Canada
    2. algonquin park ; Algonquin Park
    3. kathleen ; Kathleen
    4. albert ; Albert
    5. ottawa ; Ottawa
    6. windsor hotel ; Windsor Hotel
    7. oscar ; Oscar

D. 1. ✘ ; My sister and I like playing in the snow.
   2. ✔
   3. ✘ ; Cindy names every snowman we build.
   4. ✘ ; The biggest one is called Starlie.
   5. ✘ ; I like Witty, the smallest one, best.
   6. ✔

15 The Storybook Club

A. 1.
   2.
   3.
   4.
   5.
   6.

B. (Individual drawing and writing)
C. Day of the Week:
   Tuesday ; Sunday ; Wednesday ; Monday
   Month of the Year:
   May ; November ; July ; March
   Festival:
   Mother's Day ; Easter ; Halloween ; Thanksgiving
D. 1. I like Christmas.
   2. It is on December 25.
   3. It is on a Thursday this year.
   4. We are holding a party on Christmas Day.
   5. I will invite my friend Sandra to come.
   6. I will give her an invitation card this Friday.

16 Snow Day

A. 1. ✔
   2. ✔
   3.
   4. ✔
   5.
   6. ✔
   7. ✔
   8.
   9.

B. (Individual writing and drawing)
C. 1. ?
   2. .
   3. !
   4. . / !
   5. ?
   6. ?
   7. ?
   8. !
   9. .
D. 1. Jasmine, David, and I go swimming every Sunday.
   2. I love having toast, sausages, and milk for breakfast.
   3. Pink, blue, green, and purple are my favourite colours.
   4. You need to bring glue, scissors, and some clips to class tomorrow.
   5. Put your dolls, teddy bears, and building blocks back in the toy box.
   6. My sister likes eating pancakes with jam, honey, or maple syrup.
   7. Spring, summer, fall, and winter are the four seasons in Canada.
   8. Do you want lollipops, chocolate, or cotton candy?

17 My Mom, the Student

A. 1. a hospital
   2. healthful food
   3. nurse
   4. student
B. 1. sick
   2. meals
   3. proud
   4. Maybe
   5. study
C. 1. mom
   2. I
   3. pastries
   4. Dad
   5. neighbours
   6. Mrs. Wrights
   7. sons
   8. They

D. 1. girl
    2. brothers
    3. dog
    4. children
    5. boy

18 The Giant Turnip

A. 1. C
    2. B
    3. D
    4. A
B. 3 ; 5 ; 1 ; 6 ; 2 ; 4
C. 1. He
    2. They
    3. It
    4. She
    5. He
    6. It
D. 1. I
    2. I
    3. She
    4. I
    5. He
    6. He
    7. They
    8. We

19 Mr. Music's One-Man Band

A.

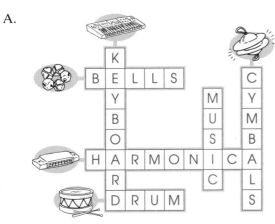

B. 1. one
    2. a drumstick
    3. on Mr. Music's ankles
    4. a harmonica
C. 1.

    2.
    3.
    4.
    5.
    6.
    7.
    8.
    9.

D. 1. holds
    2. plays
    3. strikes
    4. shakes
    5. gives
    6. claps

20 My New Dog

A.

```
        d  B  g
     e  a  n  l  o     c
  B  v  q  h  a  p  p  y  k
k  g  e  d  e  z  v  i  m  d  b
s  a  r  s  r  e  d  u  r  o  h
i  t  y  l  j  h  r  p  i  g  e
v  c     w  B  l  g  m     r  j
m  y  d  o  g     p  o  u  n  d
d  o  a  t  x  f  a  t  h  e  r
f  m  y  p  l  i  q  b  s  d  n
```

B. 1. is
    2. is
    3. am
    4. is ; is
    5. are

C. 1. are
    2. are
    3. is
    4. am
    5. is

21 Starry Starry Night

A. 1. dipper
    2. planet
    3. astronomer
    4. lopsided
    5. telescope

B. 1. He is an astronomer.
    2. He gave her a big telescope.
    3. It looks like a big pot with a long handle.
    4. "The Broken W" looks like a "w".

C.

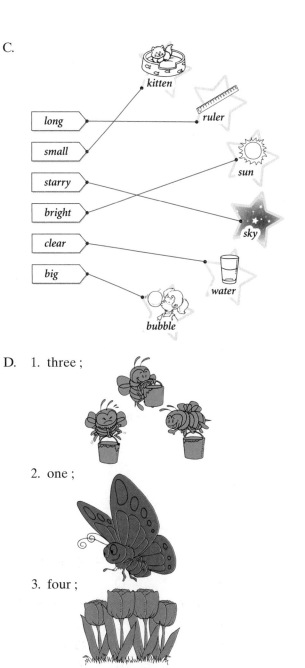

long
small
starry
bright
clear
big

kitten
ruler
sun
sky
water
bubble

D. 1. three ;

    2. one ;

    3. four ;

    4. two ;

22 Hide and Seek

A. (In any order)
2. sound ; found
3. clue ; you
4. be ; tree
5. hide ; outside
6. peek ; seek

B. 1. Hide
2. Count
3. game
4. found
5. clue

C. 1. on
2. under
3. in
4. behind
5. over

D. (Individual drawing)

23 My Wobbly Tooth

A. 1. Yesterday
2. finger
3. the Tooth Fairy
4. an apple
5. a quarter

B.

C. a : tooth ; pillow ; string ; quarter
an : apple ; oar ; onion ; elephant
the : Tooth Fairy ; sky ; world ; North Pole

D. 1. the Olympic Games
2. a dragon
3. the CN Tower
4. the Earth
5. an owl
6. an Easter egg

24 My Perfect Day

A. 1. lucky charm
2. turkey sandwich
3. singing birds
4. porridge
5. pear
6. blue dress

B. (Individual drawing and writing)

C. 1. and
2. or
3. or
4. and
5. and
6. or

D. 1. Friday or Saturday
2. Sue or Rita
3. apples and milk
4. the puzzle or the teddy bear
5. the baseball and baseball bat

25 Riddles

A. 1. a comb
2. water

B. (Individual writing and drawing)

C. 1.
2.
3. ✔
4. ✔
5. ✔
6. ✔
7.

D. 1. The movie was long ^but^ we did not find it boring.
2. This dish does not look nice ^but^ it tastes good.
3. The girls play volleyball ^but^ the boys play soccer.
4. The sun is shining ^but^ it is also raining.
5. I want to eat a Popsicle ^but^ there are not any left.

E. 1. but this one is too sour
   2. but I can reach it
   3. but it is friendly
   4. but the sea water is cool

26 The King of the Jungle

A. 1. fox
   2. deer
   3. tiger
   4. monkey
B. 1. The tiger tried to catch the fox.
   2. The fox said that he was the King of the Jungle.
   3. The deer were frightened and ran away.
   4. The monkeys also ran away.
   5. The tiger bowed to the fox.
   6. The fox ran proudly away.
C. (Colour the foxes of these sentences.)
   1. The fox was in the jungle.
   2. The fox chases the rabbit.
   3. The sun is behind the clouds.
   4. The cat is eating the fish.
D. 1. Mice like eating cheese.
   2. The flowers are colourful.
   3. She puts the toys in the box.
   4. Benny is writing a letter.
   5. Who wants strawberry ice cream?
   6. The dog is hiding the candy.
   7. Where are you going?

27 My First Visit to the Dentist

A.

k	k	a	q	t	f	d	n	r	e	r	b	l	i
b	a	y	b	p	r	e	s	s	e	d	p	a	x
c	n	e	i	z	h	x	c	o	l	j	s	w	c
u	i	c	g	b	r	j	a	z	b	a	c	k	m
s	c	a	r	e	d	y	b	c	v	m	u	t	s
n	e	u	l	r	d	n	e	h	w	o	p	e	n
t	o	o	t	h	b	r	u	s	h	p	h	o	k
t	e	v	b	u	m	s	g	a	c	z	e	w	b

B. 1. a little scared
   2. a mouse having his teeth checked
   3. in six months
C. 1. John is hungry.
   2. It is too cold to go to the beach in winter.
   3. Those puppies are cute.
D. 1. My aunt has a candy shop.
   2. He goes fishing every weekend in summer.
   3. She will get her eighth teddy bear this summer.

28 A Day with Grandpa

A.

B. 1. F
   2. E
   3. D
   4. C
   5. A
   6. B
C. 1. I got the peanut butter from the fridge.
   2. I put peanut butter over a pine cone.
   3. Then my sister rolled the pine cone in birdseed.
   4. Grandpa tied a string around the pine cone.
   5. He then tied the pine cone to a branch.
   6. Soon a bird came and pecked at the pine cone.
D. (Individual writing)
   B ; A ; C

1   What Makes Me "Me"

A.   (Individual drawing and answers)
B.   (Individual answers)

2   Special People

A.   parent: 5 ; A
    doctor: 1 ; D
    teacher: 4 ; E
    Elder: 3 ; C
    postal worker: 2 ; B
B.   (Individual drawing and answers)

3   Important Places

A.   (Individual drawing and answers)
B.   (Individual drawing and answer)

4   Special Things

A.   (Individual drawings and answers)
B.

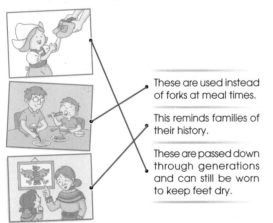

(Individual drawing and answer)

5   Special Events

A.   (Individual drawings and answers)

6   Showing Respect

A.   Check 4 and 5.
B.

cleaning

7   My Changing Roles

A.   1. grandson
    2. daughter
    3. student
    4. neighbour
B.   (Individual drawing and answers)
C.

invite him/her to my
birthday party

help tie his/her shoes

visit his/her house

comfort him/her when
he/she is sad

big brother/
sister

friend

both

8 My Changing Responsibilities

A. At Home: sister ; A ; B
    At School: student ; A ; C
B. (Individual drawings and answers)

9 More Changing Roles and Responsibilities

A. (Suggested answers)
    A. At home, you can go to the washroom whenever you like. At school, you show respect by asking your teacher for permission before you go to the washroom.
    B. At a park, you can read a story out loud. In a library, you need to speak quietly so others can study or read.
B.

(Individual answer)

10 Our Interactions with Others

A. sad ; sympathetic ; helps ; thank ; happy
B. (Suggested answers)
    A: embarassed, angry
    B: sad, upset
    C: thankful
    (Individual answer)

11 My Friends and Me

A. (Individual drawings and answers)
B. (Individual answers)

12 New Experiences

A. (Individual answers)
B. Having recess with other classes:
    1. (Individual answer)
    2. Go ; respectfully
    Doing homework:
    1. (Individual answer)
    2. Keep up ; on time

13 Helping Others

A. 1. child
    2. senior
    3. adult
B.

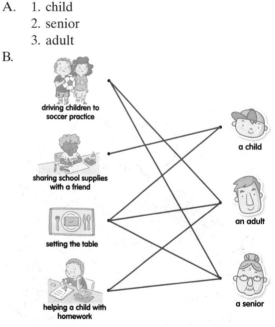

C. (Individual answer)

14 My Home

A. (Individual answers and colouring)
B. 1. (Individual answer)

2.

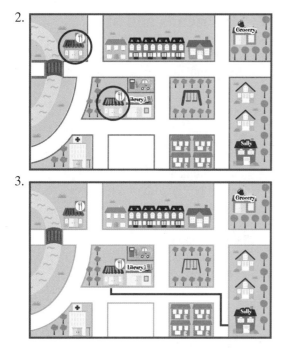

3.

4. (Individual answer)
5. (Individual drawing)

15 Nature around Me

(Suggested answers)

A.

B.

(Individual answer)

16 My Local Community

A. 1. B
    2. H
    3. I
    4. F
B. 1. Farmer's Market, Butcher Shop, Grocery Store
    2. (Individual answers)

17 Community Workers

A.

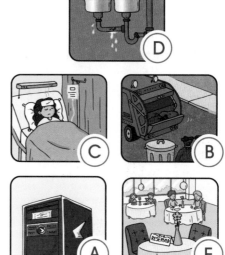

B.

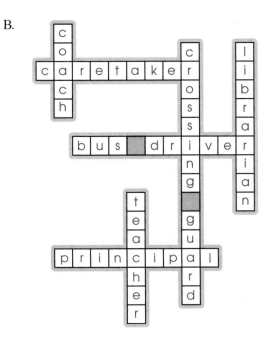

1. clean-up ; tidy
2. Donate ; charity

19 People and Their Community

A. dirty ; pests ; work ; unsafe ; (Individual answer)
B. Positive Impacts: shop ; business ; more
    Negative Impacts: animals ; plants ; less
    (Individual answer)

20 Community Changes

A. 1. (Suggested answers)
        There are more houses. ; There is a lot more
        greenery in the community. ; There are new
        businesses in the community.
    2. (Suggested answer)
        There are more houses which means more
        people can live in the community. The grocery
        shop and restaurant give people a place to
        shop and have fun in, while the park gives the
        children a place to play in.
B. 1. Day 1: 8
        Day 2: 9
        Day 3: 7
        Day 4: 12
    2. Day 4 ; because more trees were planted on
        Day 4 than any other day
    3. (Suggested answer)
        B
    4. (Suggested answer)
        Trees are also good for animals because they
        give some animals a place to live in.

18 Helping My Community

A.

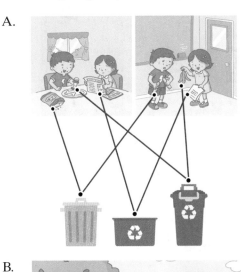

B.

21 Areas in the Community

A. 1. Residential
    2. Commercial
    3. High Traffic
    4. Recreational

B.

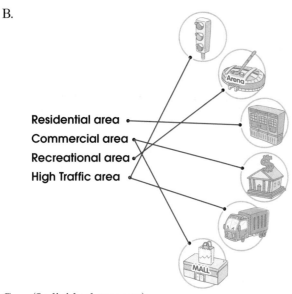

C.   (Individual answers)

22 Locating Places

A.   1. down
2. up
3. near
4. far
5. across
6. right
7. left
8. beside
B.   left ; left ; right
C.

1. far
2. near
3. left
4. right

5.

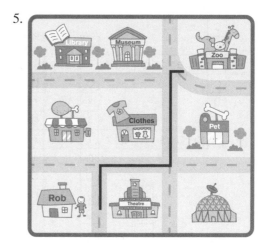

23 Using Maps

A.   1. ⌂ house ; 🛝 park
2. (Suggested drawings)

3. (Individual colouring and answer)
B.   1. 9 ; 12
2. 1
3. 2 ; up
4. go 1 block down

24 Government Workers

A.   1. H ; W
2. A ; S
3. E ; P
4. B ; R

5.

B. (Suggested answer)
    We can carefully wrap the broken glass in layers
    of newspapers to keep any sharp edges from
    sticking out and hurting the garbage collectors.

1   My Body

A.
finger	head
arm	chin
back	elbow
leg	hand
foot	knee
	toe

B.

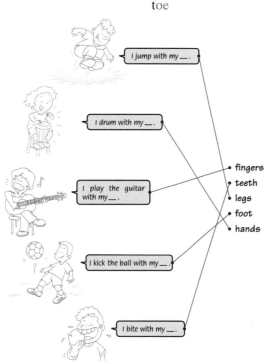

I jump with my ___ .

I drum with my ___ .

I play the guitar with my ___ .

I kick the ball with my ___ .

I bite with my ___ .

- fingers
- teeth
- legs
- foot
- hands

2   Five Senses

A.   eye ;

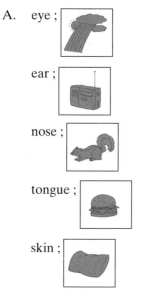

ear ;

nose ;

tongue ;

skin ;

B.
1. smell		2. nose
3. sight		4. eyes
5. touch		6. skin
7. hearing		8. ears
9. taste		10. tongue

3   Our Senses at Work

A.   1.

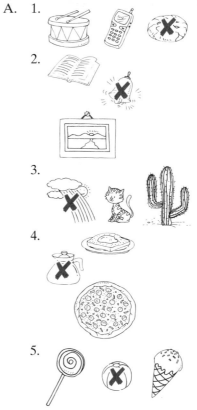

2.

3.

4.

5.

B.   Lemon: see, touch, smell, taste
Bell: see, hear, touch
Rainbow: see

C.   1. A, B, F   2. C, D, E

4   Living Things and Their Growth

A.   1.

2.

3.

4.

B.

5 Needs of Living Things

A. 1. C, D, E, I   2. B, F
    3. A, G, H
B. 1. air   2. water
    3. air   4. food
    5. water   6. food

6 Living Things and the Way They Move

A. 1. climb   2. hop
    3. swing   4. slither
    5. gallop   6. fly
    7. dive
B. 1. bouncing   2. throwing
    3. swinging   4. diving
    5. rolling

7 Patterns in Living Things

A. 1. 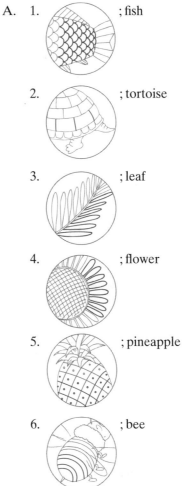 ; fish

    2. ; tortoise

    3. ; leaf

    4. ; flower

    5. ; pineapple

    6. ; bee

B. spots: E, G
    rings: C, D
    spiral: F, H
    stripes: A, B

8 Healthful Eating

A. Grain Products: B, D, G, I, K, L
    Vegetables and Fruit: A, C, J, M
    Milk and Alternatives: H, N, O
    Meat and Alternatives: E, F

B. 1.  ; juice

    2. ; popcorn

    3. ; fresh fruit

C.

9 Safe and Healthful Living

A.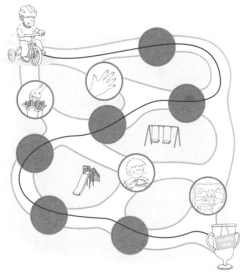

B. 1. B   2. E
    3. A   4. D
    5. C   6. F

10 Objects and Materials

A. Colour 1, 5: blue
    Colour 2, 6: yellow
    Colour 3, 8: green
    Colour 4, 7: brown

B. 1. hard   2. heavy
    3. rough   4. dark
    5. shiny

C. cement ; glass ; wood

11 Materials that Join

A. Colour the sheets with the words: mortar, thread, glue, nail, button, zipper

B. 1. D   2. B
    3. E   4. F
    5. C   6. A

12 Changing Materials

A. 1.

    2.

    3.

    4.

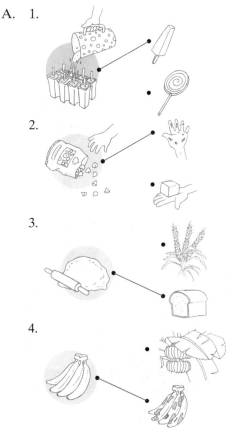

5.

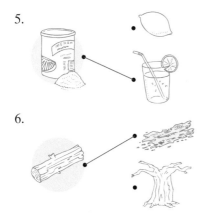

6.

B.   Project 1: A ; sticky, wet
      Project 2: A, D ; liquid, runny
      Project 3: A, B, C, D ; thick, soft

13 Reuse and Recycle

A.   Paper: G, H, I
      Aluminum: A, D, J
      Glass: B, F
      Plastic: C, E, K

B.

C.   (Individual drawings)

14 Energy and the Sun

A.   1. sun
      2. cars
      3. sailboats
      4. plants
      5. food
      6. bodies
      7. sun
      8. Earth

B.
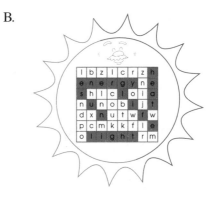

15 Energy and Food

A.

B.   grass ; grasshopper ; fox ; lion
C.   least to greatest: B ; D ; E ; A ; C

16 Smart Energy Use

A.   1. wood   2. gasoline
      3. electricity   4. wind
      5. sun
B.   1. hearing   2. touch
      3. sight
C.

17 Structures around Us

A.

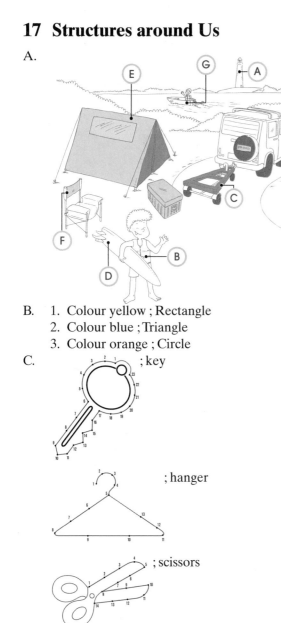

B. 1. Colour yellow ; Rectangle
   2. Colour blue ; Triangle
   3. Colour orange ; Circle

C.   ; key

            ; hanger

            ; scissors

18 Natural Structures

A. 1. A
   2. C
   3. B
   4. E
   5. F
   6. D

B. A: beaver dam
   B: spider web
   C: honeycomb

C. A ; D ; B ; C

19 Structures Together

A. 1.

2.

3.

4.

5.

B. A, B, D, E, G, J, K, L

20 Day and Night

A. 1.

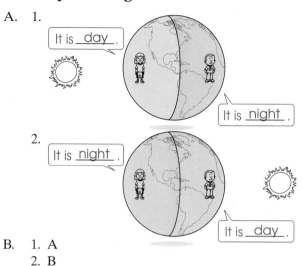

    2.

B. 1. A
    2. B
C. A ; C ; B

21 Seasons

A. Summer: Work: B, D
           Play: Q, R
    Winter: Work: A, C
           Play: P, S

B.

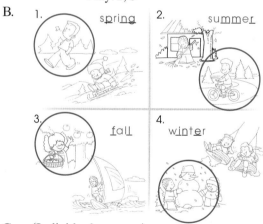

C. (Individual answers)

22 Plants through the Seasons

A. 1. winter
    2. spring
    3. fall
    4. summer
B. 1. Colour the leaf green.
    2. Colour the leaf red, brown, yellow, or orange.

C.

pea

fern

iris

tomato

23 Animals through the Seasons

A. 1. winter
    2. fall
    3. summer
    4. winter
    5. fall
    6. spring
B. 1. B
    2. C
    3. A
C. winter

24 Night Animals

A.

B. 1.

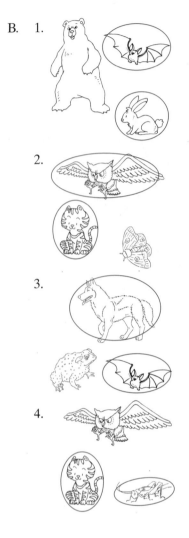

2.

3.

4.